# *Jewish Natural Nutrition…*
# *with Kabbalistic Insights*

Yaakov Levinson, MS, RD

Helm Publishing

Copyeditors: Savannah Helm, Dolly Parsons and Yoseif Meir Rich
Editor: Kathy King
Layout & cover: Pat Dodge, Pages Communications Service

It is Jewish custom not to write G-d's name in full out of
respect. This book contains many holy texts. The author
therefore requests that the book be treated with respect and
should not be used or discarded in inappropriate places.

Helm Publishing
P.O. Box 2105, Lake Dallas, TX 75065
940-497-3558 phone
940-497-2927 fax

Orders: 877-560-6025
www.HelmPublishing.com
Printed in USA

ISBN 978-0-9787829-3-1

# Dedication

To all my family members, teachers, colleagues,

and friends, and especially to the Almighty,

who has us unite body and soul in the act of eating.

# Reviews

**Professor Leon Epstein, Chairman**
Department of Social Medicine, Kiryat Hadassah, Jerusalem

Yaakov Levinson has written a very different book on nutrition and dietetics. The distinct "flavor" that distinguishes it from many other texts that crowd the bookshelves is the unique mixture that he has prepared. It melds an expert's view of nutrition and disease with its special implication and application to religious Jewish tradition.

This makes it an especially valuable text for patients and families who wish to utilize and apply nutritional knowledge to their own specific needs and within the context of their own religious mores. No less valuable is its place in the armamentarium of the health practitioner whose clientele includes religious Jews with their specific mix of nutritional needs and religious beliefs. This book will be invaluable in providing an appropriate service for them.

**Rabbi I. Scheiner**
Dean, Kamenitzer Yeshiva of Jerusalem, Jerusalem

I read with much interest the proofs of your forthcoming book, concerning diet and health from a true Jewish outlook. Your approach reveals the views of a real expert in the field, also imbued with deep feeling and reverence of Jewish values.

I remember fondly the times we spent together, while you were so devotedly helping my grandson overcome his problems. I am confident that your book will be warmly received by every Torah-true person, who is also interested in the problems of diet and health, from a Torah imbued perspective.

# Acknowledgments

My interest in nutrition was first sparked in my early teens by my late father's friend, Dr. Stanley Levine. The many teachers, professional colleagues, rabbis, students, patients, and friends who molded my career over the years would fill many pages. I thank you all. Outstanding nutrition authorities who have guided me personally include the late Dr. Janice Neville, DSc, RD, chairperson, Department of Nutrition, Case Western Reserve University, and past president of the American Dietetic Association; Dr. Edith Lerner, PhD, RD, and Dr. Grace Petot, PhD, RD, Department of Nutrition, Case Western Reserve University; and Dr. George Blackburn, MD, Deaconess Hospital (Harvard University).

Deepest thanks go to my parents, Dr. and Mrs. Max Levinson, who besides everything else, supported a professional student for so many years, and to my dear, late grandfather, Irving Jaffe, who was always there with loving encouragement.

Special thanks to my wife, Sarah Miriam, who poured much emotional and intellectual energy into this book and into my entire nutrition career. Thanks to our children, Meshullam, Chani, Esti, Aidee, Moshe, Malki, and Eli, who grew up with a father who was also an extremely busy health practitioner and Torah student.

Outstanding Torah authorities who have helped me greatly over the years with guidance, study, and blessings include, among many others, the late Grand Rabbi of Lubavitch, Menachem Mendel Schneersohn; and the late Grand Rabbi of Lelov, Moshe Mordechai Biderman, the memory of the righteous should be a blessing; the Grand Rabbi of Belz, the late Grand Rabbi of Nedvorna, Zefat, his righteous memory should be a blessing; the Grand Rabbi of Stretin, Jerusalem, the Grand Rabbi of Kamarna, Beit Shemesh; together with Rabbi Azriel Chaikin (Brussels, Kiev, Brooklyn); Rabbi Yisroel Goldberg (Brooklyn); Rabbi Benyomin Cohen (Brooklyn, Melbourne); Rabbi Yehuda Blum (Cleveland); Rabbi Leibel Teitelbaum (Antwerp); Rabbi Aaron Mordechai Rutner (Jerusalem); the late Rabbi Shalom Rosenthal of Zefat, Israel; Rabbi Avigdor Feivelson (Zefat); Rabbi Yitzchak Dovid Rutman (Jerusalem); Rabbi Shraga Samuels (Jerusalem); and fondly, my long-term study partner in Talmud, Rabbi Chaim Yosef Zlotnik of Jerusalem.

Thanks to my dear friends, Professor Leon Epstein, of Hadassah Medical School, and his wife, Aviva Epstein, past president of the Israel Dietetic Association and head dietitian of Rambam Hospital in Haifa, Israel, together with Bella Adler, statistician of Hadassah Medical School, for their consistent encouragement and invaluable professional advice and assistance. Thanks to my good friend and colleague, gerontologist Dr. Tzvi Dwolatzky, who has been a constant inspiration and motivating force throughout the years. Special thanks to my oldest, dearest friend, Yehuda Levine, for his many insights and suggestions which added depth and greatly improved the spiritual aspects of this book.

Thanks to Ilan Levin of Florum and to Menachem Shinberg of Provi Research, who is marketing the Provi nutritional formulas based on my research studies.

Special thanks to Kathy King, RD, LD, for her constant positive support and professional advice over the years which kept me moving, and for her agreeing to publish this book. I believe that her many insightful suggestions have greatly improved this book, and have made it unique.

Yaakov Levinson,
Jerusalem

# Yaakov Levinson, MS, RD

Yaakov Levinson holds a Bachelor of Arts degree (BA) in biology from Hamilton College, Clinton, New York, and earned a Master's degree (MS) in clinical nutrition from Case Western Reserve University in Cleveland, Ohio (1976). He is a former member of the American Dietetic Association, and as a nutritionist at Memorial Hospital in Albany, New York, he published a hospital manual on clinical nutrition.

In Israel, he was Director of the Nutrition Department of the Rebecca Sieff Hospital in Tzefat for five years, during which time he also taught dietetic interns from the Hebrew University of Rechovot, and lectured at the Tzefat School of Nursing and to hospital physicians on nutrition topics. He has been the nutritionist of the Surgery A and Orthopedics Department at Hadassah Medical Center, nutritionist for the Radiology Department of the Sharett Cancer Institute at Hadassah, the head dietitian at Hadassah Hospital, Mt. Scopus, and nutrition consultant at the Neve Simcha Geriatric Hospital in Jerusalem.

Levinson has presented original research at the 12th International Congress of Dietetics in Manilla, Philippines (1996) and at the 13th International Congress of Dietetics in Edinburgh, Scotland (2000), as well as at several national medical conferences in Israel. He has published two breakthrough research studies in prestigious U.S. medical journals on a geriatric nutritional formula he designed and used successfully. He is the originator of the Provi nutrition formulas, which are based on these studies.

A Torah-observant Jew, Yaakov Levinson has studied at both Hassidic and Lithuanian Torah academies in Brooklyn, Tzefat, and Jerusalem.

*Yaakov Levinson, MS, RD, in a Jewish prayer shawl with "Tephillin" (phylacteries) prayer boxes on his head and arm which contain parchments with holy writings proclaiming G-d's unity, and love of G-d.*

# Table of Contents

# Section I


# Jewish History and Food Roots

# Chapter 1

## Brief History of the Jewish People and Religion

### BACKGROUND

The Jewish people are basically an extended family, spread throughout the world, who are referred to as the Children of Israel. Our founding and first Jew, Patriarch Abraham (Avraham) broke away from his idol-worshiping father, and proclaimed G-d's Oneness to the world. His son, the Patriarch Isaac (Yitzchak) continued his father's heritage in the land of Israel, and had a son Jacob (Ya'akov), who continued in his father's ways. The Patriarch Jacob, later known as Israel (Yisroel), had children who established the twelve tribes. Their descendants, as well as the converts to Judaism, are referred to as the Children of Israel.

Due to famine in the land of Israel, Jacob's family, consisting of seventy persons, were forced to move to the land of Egypt, where they multiplied greatly but were bitterly enslaved. However, upon their redemption from Egyptian slavery, they numbered 600,000 men plus women and children. Through a miraculous G-dly redemption, the Jewish people were led out of Egypt by Moses (Moshe), and they wandered in the wilderness until G-d revealed His laws and commandments to Moses on Mount Sinai in the form of the Written and Oral Torah, which will be explained later.

After wandering in the desert for forty years under the leadership of Moses, the Twelve Tribes of Israel, the descendants of the sons and grandsons of Jacob, entered the land of Canaan at Jericho lead by Moses' successor, Joshua (Jehoshua). After conquering the land, it was distributed among them, according to their tribal heritage.

Eventually, the prophet Samuel (Shmuel) appointed Saul (Shaul) to be their king. King David (Dovid), who is famous for his psalms, succeeded Saul. David's son Solomon (Shelomo) built the first permanent Temple in the capitol city of Jerusalem. The Babylonians destroyed this First Temple in the early 6th century B.C.E. (Before the Common Era). The Jews were exiled to Babylonia, and this era is referred to as the first Jewish diaspora (scattering of people, language and culture outside Israel). Seventy years later many Jews returned to their homeland and rebuilt a new Second Temple, and reinstated the old religious practices.

In 66 C.E. (Common or Christian Era) the conquering Romans destroyed Jerusalem and the Second Temple, expelling all the Jews, which is referred to as the second Jewish diaspora. Jewish worship was no longer organized around the Temple, prayer replaced the Temple sacrifices, and individual communities were established throughout the world. Jews were then classified according to their places of exile – those settling in central and Eastern Europe were referred to as Ashkenazic Jews, and those of Spain, Portugal, and North Africa as Sephardic Jews. At the end of almost a 4000 year history, many Jews have now re-settled in the Land of Israel.


## THE JEWISH CALENDAR

The principles of the Jewish calendar have their source in the Torah, which contains several calendar-related commandments, including G-d's commandment during the Exodus from Egypt to fix the month of Nissan as the first month of the year. [*Exodus* 12:12]

The Jewish calendar is lunisolar, based on three astronomical phenomena: the Earth's rotation about its axis (a day); the moon's revolution about the Earth (a month); and the Earth's revolution around the sun (a year). The civil calendar used by most of the world does not correlate the moon cycles and the month. The Jewish calendar, on the other hand, coordinates all of the three astronomical phenomena. Months are either 29 or 30 days, relating to the 29½-day lunar cycle. Years are 12 or 13 months to correlate with the 12.4 month solar cycle.

The lunar month begins when the first glimpse of the moon becomes visible after the dark of the moon. In ancient times the new months were fixed by observation. In a strictly lunar calendar there are about 12.4 lunar months in a solar year, so a 12-month lunar year is about 11 days shorter than a solar year. To compensate for this, the Jewish calendar uses a 12-month lunar calendar with occasional addition of an extra month (a leap year). The extra month, when added, is inserted after the regular month of Adar, and it is known as "Adar Sheini" (the Second Adar).

The Jewish calendar used today is now based on mathematical and astronomical calculations to correspond to the three mentioned astronomical phenomena.

The year number on the Jewish calendar represents the number of years since Creation. It is calculated by adding up the ages of people in the Bible back to the time of Creation. To refer to the years on the civil (Gregorian) calendar, we use the abbreviations C.E. and B.C.E. (Before the Common Era). Dates before the year 1 C.E. are indicated by using B.C.E.; from 1 C.E. on are referred to as the First Century, Second Century, etc.

## Months of the Jewish Calendar

As mentioned, the first month is Nissan, in the spring, when the Passover holiday occurs. The Jewish New Year though, is in Tishrei, actually the seventh month, and it is at this time that the year number is increased.

The names of the months were established at the time of the return of the Jews to the land of Israel from the Babylonian exile, between the destruction of the First and Second Temples. The names, indicated below, are actually in Babylonian, and not in Hebrew.

| The Months of the Jewish Calendar | | |
|---|---|---|
| Number | Month | Civil Equivalent |
| 1 | Nissan | March-April |
| 2 | Iyar | April-May |
| 3 | Sivan | May-June |
| 4 | Tammuz | June-July |
| 5 | Av | July-August |
| 6 | Elul | August-September |
| 7 | Tishrei | September-October |
| 8 | Cheshvan | October-November |
| 9 | Kislev | November-December |
| 10 | Tevet | December-January |
| 11 | Shevat | January-February |
| 12 | Adar Aleph | February-March |
| 13 (leap year) | Adar Beit | February-March |

## Days of the Jewish Week

Besides the Sabbath (Shabbat or Shabbos), the name of the seventh day of the week, the Jewish calendar does not use names for the days of the week. It refers to them simply as first day, second day, etc., or "First Day of the Sabbath, Second Day of the Sabbath, etc."

The Jewish day is of no fixed length! It runs from sunset (start of "evening") to the next sunset, reflecting the Biblical verse, "…there was evening and there was morning…" [*Genesis* 1:5] in the story of Creation. There is also no clock in the Jewish calendar, so a civil clock is used as a reference point.

## THE TORAH LITERATURE

Religious beliefs and practices are expressed in the vast Jewish religious writings, collectively known as the Torah literature. The word "Torah" then, refers to the entire body of sacred Jewish literature. As mentioned previously, Jewish tradition teaches that G-d revealed His Will in the form of laws or statues, as the 613 commandments ("mitzvoth") to our greatest prophet and teacher, Moses, on Mount Sinai. The most famous of these were written on tablets of stone, and they are referred to as the Ten Commandments. All the commandments were given together in the form of a Written Torah and an Oral Torah. See Table 1.1.

| Table 1.1 Written and Oral Torah | |
| --- | --- |
| Written Torah – referred to as the "Bible" | Oral Torah – Talmud |
| Five Books of Moses *(Chumash)* are now handwritten by a scribe with ink on parchment, and this Torah scroll is placed in the ark in Jewish synagogues.<br>　　Genesis *(Bereshis)*<br>　　Exodus *(Shemos)*<br>　　Leviticus *(Vayikra)*<br>　　Numbers *(Bamidbar)*<br>　　Deuterotomy *(Devarim)*<br>Prophets<br>Writings | Mishna (six orders)<br>(See Table 1.3 for detail)<br>Gemara |

Christians refer to the Jewish Bible (the Written Law) collectively (The Five Books of Moses, the Prophets, and the Writings) as the "Old Testament." The contents and order of what is called the "Old Testament" can vary from one publisher or church denomination to another. The original text was written in Biblical Hebrew with parts in Biblical Aramaic. Changes have occurred as a result of translation of the original texts. See Table 1.2 Old Testament.

| Table 1.2 Old Testament Chapters ||
|---|---|
| **The Prophets (Nevi'im)** | **The Writings (Kesuvim)** |
| Joshua (Yehoshua) | Psalms (Tehillim) |
| Judges (Shoftim) | Proverbs (Mishlei) |
| Samuel 1 and 2 (Shmuel) | Job (Iyov) |
| Kings 1 and 2 (Malachim) | Song of Songs (Shir Ha-Shirim) |
| Isaiah (Yeshaya) | Ruth |
| Jeremiah (Yirmiyah) | Lamentations (Eicha) |
| Ezekiel (Yechezkel) - The Twelve | Ecclesiastes (Koheles) |
| Hosea (Hoshea) | Esther |
| Joel (Yoel) | Daniel |
| Amos | Ezra and Nehemiah |
| Obadiah (Ovadyah) | Chronicles (Divrei Ha-Yamim) |
| Jonah (Yonah) | |
| Nachum | |
| Habbakkuk (Chavakuk) | |
| Zephaniah (Tzefanyah) | |
| Chaggai | |
| Zechariah | |
| Malachi | |

In addition to the written scriptures there is also an Oral Torah, also known as the Oral Law. Here one finds explanations of what the written scriptures mean, and how to apply the commandments to daily life. As the rabbis feared misinterpretation or even that these oral laws would be forgotten, in the second century C.E. the oral laws were written down as the six books of the "Mishna." Over the next few centuries, commentaries on the Mishna were recorded in Jerusalem and in Babylon, which are known as the "Gemara." The Mishna and the Gemara together, completed in the fifth century C.E. are known as the "Talmud."

There have since been many commentaries on the Talmud. The rabbis' commentaries are to understand the original teachings of Moses, as recorded in the Oral Law. They are based on exacting logic and are not mere intuitive opinions. The Talmud is a forum of intensive debate among the rabbis over many generations to try to reach a consensus of the truth. At times, they even admit that the truth of the law eludes them, which adds credibility to all of their other discussions. Generally, though, an agreement is reached, and the legal decisions are codified as Jewish law.

The Mishna is divided into six sections or orders (sederim). Each order contains subdivisions called tractates (masechtot). Only about half of these tractates are now included in the Talmud. See Table 1.3.

| Table 1.3 The Mishna |
| --- |
| Seeds (Zera'im) – Agricultural laws |
| Festivals (Mo'ed) – Sabbath and holidays |
| Women (Nashim) – Marriage, divorce, contracts |
| Damages (Nezikin) – Financial laws |
| Holy Things (Kodashim) – Sacrifices and the Temple |
| Purities (Toharos) – Laws of ritual purity and impurity |

## Other Holy Writings

"Midrashim" contain stories and commentaries to derive Jewish law or to teach moral lessons from the Bible. The Midrashim were often derived from and are based on teachings of the early authors of the Talmud.

There is also a vast body of Jewish legal literature, based on the Talmud. Best known attempts to codify the massive Jewish law into an organized system are the *Mishna Torah* by Maimonides, and the *Shulchan Aruch* by Rabbi Joseph Caro. In addition, there are many other abbreviated or specialized legal texts, such as the *Kitzur Shulchan Aruch*.

Also, there are many books of Jewish philosophy, such as the ethical or "mussar" texts and Hassidic publications, written by disciples of Rabbi Israel Baal Shem Tov, founder of the Hassidic movement.

There is, as well, a highly developed mystical tradition known as "kabbalah," which will be discussed in detail in the following section, due to its special relevance to our topic.

Kabbalah are the teachings to explain the inner meaning of both the Bible and rabbinical literature, as well as to give insights into the significance of Jewish religious practices. The proper study of kabbalah affects the manner in which a Jew observes the commandments, and it influences one to live life on a deeper level of understanding.

The discussion of the Seven Species of the Land of Israel and their connection to the ten kabbalistic sefirot is presented in a separate chapter and is an example of an insight according to Jewish mysticism.

## THE ROLE OF WOMEN IN TORAH

Torah law requires a woman to study all of the laws to observe the commandments which she is obligated to fulfill. This includes a vast array of topics, including the laws of the Sabbath, Kashrut (keeping a Kosher kitchen), and Family Purity, as well as many others. Women must also know some of the Torah's mystical teachings in order to properly fulfill the commandments of knowing G-d, loving G-d, fearing G-d, and others, which she must be constantly aware of throughout her day.

The equality of men and women in Torah begins at the highest possible level. G-d in Judaism has never been considered as exclusively male or masculine. The Torah teaches that G-d has both masculine and feminine attributes. The Bible teaches us that both man and woman were created in the image of G-d. [*Genesis* 1:27]

Traditionally in Judaism, women's responsibilities are different from men's, separate but equal in value, with more emphasis on running the household and on bringing up children. Reflecting this, women, according to the Torah, are exempted from all positive commandments ("thou shalts" as opposed to "thou shalt nots") that are time-related (must be performed at a specific time of day or year). This is because her responsibilities as a wife and mother are so important that the Torah does not require her to postpone them, even to fulfill a commandment! However, she is generally permitted to observe such commandments if she chooses, but she is not required.

The role of men in Judaism emphasizes their responsibility for Torah study. Thus, the roles are generally divided in this way, but there are exceptions. Some men are more domestically oriented, and some women are much more scholarly. Throughout the generations, there have been women with outstanding Torah knowledge. The Talmud often cites Bruria whose opinions on Jewish law were at times accepted over her male contemporaries. Miriam was one of the liberators of the Jewish people from Egyptian bondage, along with her brothers Moses and Aaron. One of the judges in the "Prophets," Deborah, was a woman. Seven of the fifty-five prophets of the Bible were women.

Recent generations have witnessed the development of schools and institutions for Torah education for Jewish girls and women on a high scholastic level. Many married, Torah-observant women work as teachers in the various religious schools. As well, they are working as doctors and health professionals, lawyers, accountants, business owners, authors, and on and on.

Jewish life, in general, though, centers around the home, and not the synagogue or one's occupation, and the observant Jewish woman is the manager of the household.

# Chapter 2

## Jewish Roots for Natural Nutrition

### BRIEF HISTORY OF JEWISH NUTRITION ROOTS

Food and other healthy habits are part of the Jewish way of life. From the history of the Jewish people we can find the roots and can trace the development of Jewish natural nutrition.

After the creation of the world, Jewish tradition teaches us in the Bible that the first man and woman, Adam and Eve, resided in a paradise, referred to as the Garden of Eden.

> And G-d said, Behold I have given you my herb bearing
> seed, which is upon the face of all the earth, and every
> tree, on which is the fruit yielding seed; to you it shall be
> for food. [*Genesis* 1:29]

Man was originally commanded to be strictly vegetarian. However, there were two special trees in the garden, one of which, the Tree of Life, would provide eternal life but Man has never eaten from it. The other, the Tree of Knowledge of Good and Evil, Man was commanded by G-d not to eat. Nevertheless, Man fell to his desire and ate from this tree. And therefore until this day, we are destined to work hard for our food in order to endure.

The next nutritional development came in the days of Noah who was a righteous man. G-d saved Noah and his family along with representatives of all the other creatures by commanding Noah to build an ark. G-d destroyed the evil which had developed in this generation by bringing a terrifying flood which devastated the entire world. Only Noah, his family, and the animals he brought with him were saved.

It was at this time, that G-d, in His mercy, permitted Man to eat meat, as it says in the Bible:

> Every moving thing that lives shall be food for you; even as the green herb have I given you all things. [*Genesis* 9:3]

G-d commanded Noah and his descendants to follow just seven rules, which apply to this day. All people of all nations would be considered righteous if they follow them, and they would be guaranteed a place in the World-to-Come, where there will be only good and peace. These rules are summarized, as follows, by the late Lubavitcher Rebbe, Rabbi Menachem Mendel Schneerson, of blessed memory:

1. Acknowledge that there is only one G-d, who is Infinite and Supreme above all things. Do not replace that Supreme Being with finite idols, be it yourself, or other beings. This command includes such acts as prayer, study, and meditation.

2. Respect the Creator. As frustrated and angry as you may be, do not vent it by cursing your Maker.

3. Respect human life. Every human being is an entire world. To save a life is to save that entire world. To destroy a life is to destroy an entire world. To help others is a corollary of this principle.

4. Respect the institution of marriage. Marriage is a most Divine act. The marriage of a man and a woman is a reflection of the oneness of G-d and His creation. Disloyalty in marriage is an assault on that oneness.

5. Respect the rights and property of others. Be honest in all your business dealings. By relying on G-d rather than on our own conniving, we express our trust in Him as the Provider of Life.

6. Respect G-d's creatures. At first, Man was forbidden to consume meat. After the Great Flood, he was permitted—but with a warning: Do not cause unnecessary suffering to any creature.

7. Maintain justice. Justice is G-d's business, but we are given the charge to lay down necessary laws and enforce them whenever we can. When we right the wrongs of society, we are acting as partners in the act of sustaining the creation.

As told earlier, Abraham, the first Jew, became the first Patriarch and founder of the Jewish people. He lived in the Land of Israel, where he helped people become aware of G-d through his hospitality and feeding a multitude of guests. Abraham's son, Isaac, became the second Patriarch and his grandson, Jacob, was the third. Jealousy arose among the sons of Jacob when he gave special attention to one son, Joseph. The brothers put Joseph into a deep hole in the ground, and he was then taken captive by a passing caravan and brought to Egypt. In Egypt, Joseph rose to a position of greatness, only second to the ruling Pharaoh, and his advice to store food saved Egypt from a world famine. Jacob and his remaining family moved to Egypt, where they were re-united with Joseph, and they were thereby saved from the famine but were forced to serve the Egyptians with back-breaking labor. Ten miracles, known as the Ten Plagues, were sent by G-d to break the Egyptian nation. The Jewish people, led by Moses, were then taken out of Egypt through the miraculous splitting of the Red Sea.

The Jews left Egypt in a hurry, and tradition teaches that they took the bread dough (which did not have time to rise) along with them on their journey for food. The "matzoh," a thin, cracker of unleavened bread, which Jews now eat on the Passover holiday, is symbolic of the original desert sun-baked dough. The booths that many Jews now build and dwell in during the fall harvest holiday, Sukkot, is also symbolic of the portable huts that the Jews lived in during their journey through the desert.

The Jewish nation wandered in the Sinai desert for forty years, where G-d miraculously supplied them with manna, a perfect food which fell from Heaven each night. Much more will be shared about this special food in Chapter 9. On Friday, a double portion of manna fell, so the Jews would have food for Saturday, the Jewish Sabbath. Chapter 8 is devoted to special Sabbath nourishment.

G-d revealed His laws and commandments to Moses and the Jewish people at Mount Sinai, this event is celebrated as the Shavout holiday. It's also called the Festival of Weeks and it takes place in the spring about seven weeks after Passover. When this event happened, the kosher system of eating was introduced and there was a strict separation of milk and meat-containing foods. Chapter 3 will cover the kosher system.

Joshua led the Jews back to the Land of Israel, which was known for its Seven Species of grains and fruits. The species will be explored together with their kabbalistic implications in Chapter 6.

After many generations, the Jewish king, David, had a son named Solomon, who eventually became king, and built the First Temple in Jerusalem. This Temple was destroyed by the conquering Babylonians, and the Jews fled the Land of Israel. After seventy years of exile the Jews then returned again, and the Second Temple was built.

With the destruction of the Second Temple by the Romans, the Jewish nation was expelled once again, and the second Jewish diaspora began and traditional foods began to change. As mentioned earlier, Jews settling in Spain, Portugal and North Africa became known as Sephardic Jews; those of Germany, Central and Eastern Europe were known as Ashkenazic Jews. The first Jews to settle in the United States were Sephardic Jews. Thereafter, the U.S. immigration was predominantly of Ashkenazic Jews.

The cuisine of both groups differs greatly, depending upon their place of residence and the surrounding climate. The Sephardic Jews generally settled in warm climates, and their foods tend to be lighter. Ashkenazic Jews lived in colder climates, and their foods were much heavier and high in fat. Recipes representative of each of these two groups can be found in Section IV under "Traditional Jewish Foods" and "Holiday Foods." At present, Sephardic and Ashkenazic Jews are returning from the exile and are living together in the Land of Israel, where foods representative of both groups can now be found.

The Saturday night meal, referred to as King David's Meal or "Melava Malka" in Hebrew, is celebrated by both Sephardic and Ashkenazic Jews and is representative of the final redemption. In Chapter 9, we learn that in the World-to-Come, the righteous will celebrate at a special feast.

Jewish tradition tells us that in the World-to-Come, the trees will regain the complete strength that they once possessed in the Garden of Eden. Having come full circle, then, all trees will again bear fruit and be loaded with cakes, as they had been at the beginning of Creation, and there will be no lack of food.

# Chronological Summary of Jewish Nutrition

### Creation of the World (25 of Elul - First Day of Creation)

### Garden of Eden: Adam and Eve
Tree of Life
Tree of Knowledge of Good and Evil
Trees with Cakes and Fruits
Taste of Manna

### Fleeing Egyptian Slavery (Passover Holiday)
Matzoh – Taste of Manna (Seder Meal)

### Wandering in Sinai Desert 40 Years (nourished by Manna)
(Sukkot Holiday- Festival of Booths)

### Weekly Sabbath Nourishment: Three Meals
Representative of the Manna

### Receiving the Torah at Mount Sinai
(Shavuot Holiday – Festival of Weeks)
Kosher System of Eating (separation of milk and meat)

### Entering the Holy Land
Species of the Land of Israel: Grains and Fruits
(10 Sefirot and Divine Flow of Sustenance)

### King David's Meal (Melava Malka)

### World-to-Come
Feast of the Righteous
Return to Trees with Cakes and Fruits

## BIBLICAL SOURCE FOR JEWISH NATURAL NUTRITION

The typical diet of Biblical times brings us back to our spiritual and nutritional roots. Upon close examination we can find in the Biblical diet the source of today's Jewish natural nutrition! The Bible, when referring to the produce of Israel, speaks of three main categories of foods: grain, wine, and oil. [*Deuteronomy* 7:13]

Grains appear to have been the main staple during Biblical times. Five types of grain are mentioned including wheat, barley, oats, rye, and spelt. Whole grains were often ground to flour for bread, which has always had very significant importance in Judaism.

Fruits eaten in Biblical times included the special fruits of the Land of Israel. They included grapes, figs, pomegranates, and dates. Olives were pressed and used as a source of oil. Sesame seeds, as well, were collected and made into oil. Other nuts and seeds used included almonds, walnuts and carobs.

Lentils appear to have been the main legumes used, together with beans. Vegetables included cucumbers, onions, and garlic.

Wine has always been an especially cherished beverage in Judaism, and it is often used in religious practices. Goat and sheep milk was commonly used at this time, as opposed to cow's milk.

Meat was apparently eaten in only small amounts, coming mainly from sheep and goats and just occasionally from cattle. Meat was generally reserved for holidays and for family celebrations.

In short, nutrition in Biblical times included whole grains, legumes, fruits and nuts, vegetables, olive and sesame oils, wine, goat and sheep milk, and small quantities of meat.

In "Guidelines for Natural Nutrition," Chapter 12, we shall see in detail how the current nutritional recommendations are rooted in these early, healthy food habits of Biblical times.

The Torah encourages good health habits, in general, as illustrated by the Biblical edict:

Be extremely protective of your lives. [*Deuteronomy* 4:15]

The great commentator Maimonides, himself an expert physician, discusses at length the importance of a healthy, balanced diet and healthy lifestyle in general. The discussion of his teachings that follows gives us a summary of the Jewish approach to health and nutrition based on Torah principles.

## THE RAMBAM – FATHER OF JEWISH NATURAL NUTRITION

Rabbi Moshe ben Maimon (known by the acronym the RAMBAM, and also as Maimonides) was born in Cordova, Spain, in 1135 C.E. Due to religious persecution, he moved first to southern Spain and then to Fez, Morocco, where he studied medicine with such famous physicians as Ibn Zuhr and Abu Yusuf. At age thirty he left for Egypt, where he lived for the remaining thirty-nine years of his life.

The Rambam wrote ten medical works, but he was especially esteemed as one of the greatest Torah authorities of all times. His expertise and writings included all areas of Jewish law and philosophy. He passed away in 1204 C.E. in Cairo and was laid to rest in Tiberias, Israel, after an illustrious, prolific religious and medical career.

The Rambam's medical writings contain the Jewish roots of today's system of natural nutrition. Our modern approach is basically an extension of his main principles and teachings. He emphasized the importance of preventive medicine and disease prevention. He foreshadowed today's "discovery" of the effect of proper lifestyle, discussing the role of diet and exercise. Mind-body interaction was primary in his approach to illness and wellness.

His medical writings were based on Jewish Talmudic sources as well as on secular, non-Jewish teachings. The Rambam wrote that all our actions should be only for the sake of G-d. We cannot live without eating or drinking. Nevertheless, we should eat and drink with the intention of preserving the health of our bodies. To achieve this aim, the Rambam advocated eating health-giving foods and the avoidance of eating as a response to purely animalistic desires. He considered efforts to ensure a healthy body the way of G-dliness and not separate from Judaism. He also added that we should avoid those practices that weaken and destroy our bodies.

To preserve health the Rambam taught that we should eat only when genuinely hungry and drink when truly thirsty. Drinking during meals should be minimized to avoid diluting the digestive juices. The preservation of good health rests on the avoidance of overeating, which he refers to as "the poison of death" and the cause of most illness. He taught us that eating a little of bad foods is actually less harmful than eating too much good and healthy food.

He advocated some exercise before eating to warm the body for improved digestion, and in general taught that exercise removes the harm caused by most bad habits that most people have. Meals should be eaten while sitting or reclining, and we should rest after meals for good digestion. Avoidance of constipation is essential for good health. Eating according to the seasons was also promoted, with cool foods and lesser quantity in the summer and warm, spicier foods in greater quantity in the winter.

Whole-grain bread was cited by the Rambam as "the best of food." The bread must not be made of refined flour and should consist of rough grain, unchaffed and unpolished. He taught that white bread or bread made of refined flour was not a good food.

Poultry was promoted over red meat as lighter and more rapidly digested. All heavy, fatty meats are called "bad." Fatty cheeses, as well, are listed as "bad foods," but fresh, low-fat cheeses are recommended.

The Rambam cautions us against overeating fruits. On the other hand, he says that figs, grapes, and almonds are always good, and we know these are rich in nutrients and phytonutrients. Unripe fruits, he claims, are like swords to the body and should be avoided.

The Rambam, in short, stressed that most illness results from eating bad foods or from overeating, even good foods. These teachings are our Jewish roots for natural nutrition.

# Chapter 3

## The Kosher System of Eating and Holiday Foods

### THE KOSHER SYSTEM OF EATING

Jewish tradition provides us with a system of eating that is appropriate for our spiritual makeup, given by the One who created our bodies and souls. This system of dietary laws is known as kashrus (or kashrut) and has its origins in the Torah. Foods that are fit or permitted for Jews to eat are called "kosher." The system is appropriate for our spiritual needs; and whatever physical or health benefits that may exist, are not the basis for this manner or tradition of eating. Of course, as we have mentioned throughout this book, our nourishment is a combination of spiritual and physical components, and these aspects are inseparable. The rabbis have told us that eating kosher helps us to be more sensitive and open to spiritual matters. So, with this wonderful system of G-d given guidelines for eating, we can elevate our souls together with the foods we eat, and gain holiness by eating in a kosher manner.

Kashrut, then refers to the body of Jewish law dealing with what foods are eaten and those to avoid, according to Jewish tradition. The term kashrut comes from the Hebrew root "kaf-shin-reish," meaning fit or proper. It is the same root as the word kosher, which describes food that meets these standards. The word kosher has entered the English language, meaning proper, fair, or acceptable. So, in addition to food, one may think of kosher business, kosher speech, kosher family life, kosher in all areas, living up to the Torah's standards.

Contrary to popular misconception, rabbis do not bless foods to make them kosher. Food is kosher that conforms to the Torah's standards. As well, there is no such thing as kosher-style food. Kosher does not indicate a style of cooking. Chinese and Italian food, for example, can also be kosher if prepared according to Jewish law, and there are many fine restaurants with these types of food throughout the world. Kosher-style usually refers to traditional Jewish foods, but not necessarily, and often they are not kosher according to Torah standards. Food that is not kosher is referred to as treif (torn), referring to the commandment not to eat animals that have been torn by other animals.

Many of the laws of kashrut are learned from the Torah's Books of Leviticus and Deuteronomy, and their details are outlined in the oral law (the Mishnah and the Gemorah, known as the Talmud). The laws were later codified in the *Shulchan Aruch* (The Code of Jewish Law) and in other authoritative texts. The Torah does not state the reason for the kashrut laws, and ultimately, the reason for their observance according to Jewish tradition, is because the Torah says so. Nevertheless, many interesting theories have been proposed to explain benefits for following these laws, such as improved hygiene and health effects. There is no reason to assume, though, that rabbit meat (never kosher) is less healthy than cow meat. Some offer the idea that the rules teach one self-control, distinction of right from wrong, and the values of good and evil. The laws of kashrut maybe thought to elevate the physical act of eating to a spiritual, religious act, which is the case, but this is not the sole reason for observing kashrut.

A summary discussion of the kosher system will be presented here, but more detailed discussion can be found in the Talmud [*Chullin*] and *Shulchan Aruch* [Yoreh Deah]. To learn how to practically apply this system of eating there are various summary texts. It is recommended that a qualified rabbi be consulted for personalized advice.

## THE KOSHER LAWS

Milk and meat are not eaten in the same meal, nor can they be prepared or served with the same dishes or utensils. After meat is eaten, time from one meal to the next must pass before eating dairy foods. Most authorities say this is six hours, but there are other customs, as well. In contrast, milk may be consumed just before eating meat after cleaning one's hands and mouth, although some have the custom to wait thirty minutes to one hour. A waiting period of six hours is sometimes applicable after eating certain hard cheeses before meat is eaten.

To keep meat and milk separate, Jewish homes keep two separate sets of cooking utensils, dishes, and silverware. The separation applies, as well, to dishwashing and to dish towels. Meals are therefore meat meals (fleishig, basari) or dairy meals (milchig, chalavi). Pareve (neutral: non-meat, non-milk) foods may be eaten with either type of meals (examples of pareve foods include: bread, grains, fruits, vegetables, fish, eggs, oils, sugars, etc.).

Kosher meat comes only from those animals specified in the Torah as "clean," or acceptable; they are those that chew their cud and have cloven (divided) hooves. Beef cattle, sheep, oxen, goats, and deer are considered acceptable. In addition, domestic fowl like chicken are acceptable and certain species of wild fowl, as well.

Pork, winged insects, reptiles, creeping animals, and birds of prey are not kosher. All permitted foods, in addition, must also be insect and worm-free when used. Eggs of a non-kosher bird are prohibited. An egg containing a blood-spot should not be eaten.

The slaughter of kosher animals is performed by a trained rabbi called a shochet. The animal's life is taken with a specially sharpened knife in the most merciful manner. Blood is not eaten and it is referred to as "the life of the animal" in the Torah.

The maximum amount of blood is drained away after the slaughtering. Meat is then soaked in water for thirty minutes, then salted on all surfaces with a medium-coarse salt, allowed to drain for almost an hour, and then washed three times to remove the salt. Hindquarter cuts are usable only if the hip sinew (gid ha-nasheh) of the thigh and certain fats and veins are removed by a qualified person. Blood from the liver cannot be removed by the soaking process. Liver must be cut and broiled on a rack, which allows the blood to drip off from the liver as it cooks. Meat and poultry when purchased should only be obtained from those butcher shops that possess a license from a rabbinical authority.

Milk of non-kosher animals is prohibited. Cholov yisroel dairy products are those whose total preparation is supervised by reliable Jewish authorities. There may be problems with rennin and gelatin made from an animal source used in making some yogurts, ice creams, and other frozen desserts, so these also require certification.

Kosher fish are those having both fins and scales. Fish with scales that cannot be detached from their skin are likewise not kosher. Shellfish, catfish, frogs, and shark meat are examples of prohibited fish. The roe (eggs) of non-kosher fish are likewise forbidden. Fish, unlike meat, do not require ritual slaughtering.

The internal fat of non-kosher animals is forbidden. Therefore, soaps to wash dishes made from animal fats are not used in food preparation. For cooking, vegetable fats and oils are acceptable.

In Israel, additional rules apply to fruits and vegetables, such as shmittah (the Sabbatical year, when most agricultural work is prohibited, once every seven years) and orleh (new fruits forbidden from trees younger than three years, which applies outside of Israel, as well).

In addition, there are laws regarding food tithes, terumah (originally the Cohen priest's due in the olden times of the Jerusalem Temple), maaser rishon (originally the Levites's due), terumas maser (originally given by the Levi to the Cohen), maser sheni, and maser ani. From food grown in the first, second, fourth, and fifth year of the seven year Shemittah cycle, a tenth becomes maser sheni, originally eaten by the owner upon visiting

Jerusalem. In foods grown in the third and sixth year of the cycle, a tenth was originally given to the poor as maser ani. As these rules must be studied in great detail, it is recommended that fruits and vegetables from the Land of Israel be purchased with rabbinical supervision. As well, only wine or grape products produced under rabbinical supervision are used.

## Kosher Certification

Prepared products are acceptable if produced within kosher standards, which generally must be indicated by a special kosher insignia on the sealed package. Keeping kosher, then, is greatly simplified by the widespread use of kashrut certification. Products certified as kosher are labeled with a symbol called a "hekhsher" (from the same Hebrew root as the word kosher, meaning fit). The symbol identifies the rabbi or organization that certifies the product. There are many certifications available, from varying locations in the world and of varying degrees of strictness. People observing kashrut may select products in relation to their recognition of the certifying body or according to their level of religious observance.

There are, at times, various opinions on a point of degree of kashrut, and there are observant persons who may choose to follow the stricter opinion. The views of the certifying organization are generally known among those that are particular in these matters, and they choose the certifications according to their religious or even political affiliations, depending upon which religious sect they belong to. This, in addition to local products available, explains why there are a great number of kosher insignias in the marketplace.

All kosher certification marks are trademarked and cannot be used except by the certifying organization. The exception to this is the letter "K" alone, which cannot be trademarked. Some companies may put a plain letter "K" on their products, but this is no proof that these products are actually kosher, as there is no third-party supervision.

It is becoming common that certifying organizations will also indicate if a product contains milk, meat or is pareve and can therefore be eaten with both. Most commonly, if the product is dairy it may have a "D" or the word "Dairy" next to the kashrut symbol. If the cow or goat is supervised by an observant Jew during the milking, the words Chalav Yisroel (Jewish milk) will be added. Products containing meat may have the word "Meat" or "M" near the symbol. A letter "P" alone next to the symbol means that it is kosher for Passover, and that it does not contain leavening. If no indication is added next to the kosher insignia, one should carefully read the ingredient list to ascertain if the product is meat, dairy or pareve (neutral).


## THE KOSHER KITCHEN

A kosher home is an important foundation of Jewish life. Let's go through a tour of a typical kosher kitchen to give you some idea of what's involved. Since a total separation of dairy and meat are required in the kosher kitchen, separate sets of dishes, pots, silverware, serving dishes, and salt shakers are essential. It is customary to use distinct colors and patterns to distinguish milchig or dairy and fleishig or meat vessels and utensils. Often red is used for meat and blue for dairy. The different sets are generally stored in separate cabinets. Separate sets of drain boards and racks, dish sponges, scouring pads, dish towels, and tablecloths are used. Dish soap, cleanser, and scouring pads used for cleaning pots and dishes all have a kosher certification (hechsher).

Separate sinks, dairy and meat, for washing dishes and for food preparation are preferred. Separate but adjoining sinks should have a barrier between them to prevent splashing from one to the other. If a single sink is used, there should be separate dish pans, one for dairy and one for meat, resting on elevated racks in which dishes are washed. The inside of the sink is considered non-kosher if only one sink is used, or if sinks previously used for non-kosher cooking are used. The table can be used at different times for meat and dairy, if one uses different tablecloths or placemats. Ideally, there are separate countertops or work areas for dairy and meat. When only one area is used for both, separate coverings are employed.

If we open the refrigerator or freezer door, we see separate areas for dairy and for meat foods. We see that care is taken so foods do not drip, thereby causing a mixing of dairy and meat foods. Hot foods are not put into the refrigerator, since this may cause problems in kashrut. For example, if a lot of milk spills into a hot pot with meat, this may cause the pot and possibly also the meat to become unkosher, and a qualified rabbi should be consulted.

When heat is involved, the laws of accidental mixture of meat and dairy foods are more strict. Extra precautions are therefore taken with the stove and oven. In the ideal situation there will be two stoves, one for dairy and one for meat foods. When only one stove is used, separate burners for dairy or meat cooking are preferred. At the least, the burners must be kept very clean. It is best to avoid cooking both dairy and meat foods at the same time on the stove, so that there is no mixing of food or steam.

Likewise, it is best to have two separate ovens.  If one oven is used, it can be kept pareve, or neutral,  not dairy or meat. All meat or dairy foods cooked in such an oven, at separate times, must be kept tightly covered all around. Since the laws for using an oven for both meat and dairy even at separate times are complex, a qualified rabbi should be consulted.

Dishwashers should be designated for either dairy or meat. Generally, separate microwave and toaster ovens are used.

In any kosher kitchen it is natural for questions to arise. For example, what do you do if you stir a pot of meat with a dairy spoon? It is important to ask a competent rabbi when any question occurs. The utensils and food in question are set aside until the question has been answered, and we find out what Jewish law says to do. The utensils in question may sometimes simply be rinsed in cold water. Sometimes the utensil can be made kosher again; sometimes the food may be eaten, sometimes not.

Before dishes and utensils are used in a kosher kitchen, they are generally immersed in a kosher ritual pool or mikvah. The mikvah is specially constructed according to Jewish law and is connected to a source of pure rain water. Vessels may also be immersed in natural bodies of water like the ocean. Disposable dishes and utensils do not require immersion.

## JEWISH HOLIDAY FOODS

Food plays an important role in the observance of the Jewish Sabbath and holidays. Foods preferred and included may be strongly influenced by one's family country of origin.

On the Sabbath (also known as Shabbos or Shabbat) no food may be cooked. The Sabbath extends from sundown Friday until Saturday night, when three closely-located stars are seen in the evening sky. Food is cooked in advance, so that the Sabbath can be dedicated as a day of rest. The Sabbath meal on Friday night is the most significant meal of the week. Two loaves of bread served at each of the three Sabbath meals signify the double portion of manna provided on Fridays during the forty years that the Jews wandered in the Sinai wilderness before Moses was given the Torah at Mount Sinai.

## Rosh Hashana

Food has symbolic meanings on Jewish holidays, as well. The most solemn of these are the first few days of the Hebrew month of Tishrei (in September or October of each year according to the solar calendar), which begins with Rosh Hashana, the Day of Judgment, and then Yom Kippur, the Day of Atonement.

Rosh Hashana, Hebrew for the "head of the year," is the Jewish New Year. It is observed on the first two days of the Hebrew month of Tishrei. Allegorically, at this time, three books of account are opened by G-d, wherein are recorded the fate of the righteous, those of intermediate status, and the wicked. The righteous are immediately inscribed by G-d in the book of life, the wicked are removed from the book of the living, and the intermediate class are given a respite of ten days to repent until the Yom Kippur holiday.

Traditionally, a trumpet made from a ram's horn, known in Hebrew as a shofar, is blown repeatedly during the Rosh Hashana prayers to arouse us to repentance and to nullify any harsh judgment. The sounding of the shofar also signifies the coronation of the king, as we proclaim G-d as King of the Universe on this day.

The challah bread for Rosh Hashana is made round, to symbolize a crown, also representative of the coronation. A wish for a sweet New Year is symbolized by dipping the bread and apples in honey. Spiritual significances of the apple are discussed in Chapter 7. The head of a fish or other animal is served to symbolize the "head" of the year. Other foods, symbolic of a good year, may also be included, depending upon the customs of the various communities. In general, sour foods are avoided, and sweet foods are eaten to further symbolize our desire for a sweet and good year.

## Yom Kippur

The holiest day of the Jewish year, Yom Kippur in Hebrew, translated as the Day of Atonement, comes on the tenth day of the Hebrew month of Tishrei. On this day, tradition teaches that the verdict decided on Rosh Hashana is sealed. It is a day of complete fasting for all except boys before the age of thirteen, girls before twelve, and people who are ill, who a competent rabbinical authority in conjunction with a medical doctor decide would be at risk if food and drink were withheld. The day is generally spent in the synagogue in prayer.

Traditionally, Jews eat two large festive meals on the day before Yom Kippur, give charity, and ask forgiveness from others whom they may have wronged.

## Sukkot

Known as the Feast of Booths or Tabernacles, the holiday of Sukkot is celebrated from the 15th to the 22nd of Tishrei (until the 23rd of Tishrei outside of Israel). It is one of the Biblical "three holidays" on which the Jews made pilgrimages to the Temple in Jerusalem, along with the Passover and Shavuout holidays. The word Sukkot is plural for the Hebrew word sukkah, meaning booth or hut. The sukkah in which Jews live and eat during the entire holiday is symbolic of the huts that the Jews lived in during their forty years of wandering in the desert after their Exodus from Egypt.

As mentioned earlier, during the holiday all meals are generally eaten in the sukkah. Traditionally, stuffed foods are eaten to symbolize our enclosure in the sukkah during this holiday. Ashkenazic Jews traditionally eat such foods as kreplach, Yiddish for chopped meat contained in dough which is boiled, or holishkess, chopped meat rolled in cabbage leaves. Strudel cakes are often eaten, as well.

## Hanukkah

Chanukah or Hanukkah (Hebrew for "dedication") is also known as the Festival of Lights. Starting on the 25th of the Hebrew month of Kislev and continuing for eight days until the 2nd of Tevet, it is a holiday commemorating the rededication of the Second Temple in Jerusalem, after the Maccabean Revolt of the 2nd century B.C.E.

The holiday is observed lighting a special nine-branched candelabrum, known in Hebrew as a menorah. One additional light is lit on each night of the holiday, using a special extra light called a shamash, which is given a separate location aside from the rest. Starting on the right, an extra light is lit each night, one on the first night, two on the second, and so on, until eight lights are lit on the eighth and final night.

Tradition teaches that after the Maccabees military victory, there was found only enough consecrated olive oil to fuel the eternal flame in the Temple's menorah for just one day. Miraculously, the oil burned for eight days, and our lighting each night for eight days symbolizes this miraculous occurrence.

Dairy foods are eaten to remember how Judith (Yehudit), daughter of Yochanon the head priest, saved the Jewish people at this time. She fed cheese to the leader of the oppressing Greeks to make him thirsty. She then gave him wine to intoxicate him, and when he fell asleep she cut off his head with his sword. Hearing this, the enemy fled and the Jewish people were saved!

In addition, it is customary to eat oily and fried foods, as the original miracle of the Hanukkah menorah involved the discovery of the small flask of olive oil. Fried potato pancakes, or latkes in Yiddish, are traditional in Ashkenazic homes. Jelly doughnuts, as well, are eaten.

## Tu b'Shevat

Tu b'Shevat, Hebrew for the 15th of Shevat, is known as the New Year of the Trees. This special holiday is discussed in detail in Chapter 4. Fresh and dried fruits, and nuts are traditionally eaten on this holiday.

## Purim

Purim, Hebrew for "lots," is a holiday that commemorates the fall of Haman the Agagite, chief minister to King Ahasuerus of Persia, and defeat of his plan to kill all the Jews in the world. The deliverance came through Mordechai and Esther, Ahasuerus' Queen, who was of royal Jewish decent. It is celebrated on the 14th day of the Hebrew month of Adar (the 15th of Adar in Jerusalem, known as Shushan Purim). The holiday is characterized by public readings of the Book of Esther, which describes in detail the Purim miracle of redemption, plus giving charity to the poor, and exchanging gifts of food among family and friends. Other customs include drinking wine, wearing masks and costumes, and public festivity in general.

Traditionally, each Jew sends two different ready-to-eat foods to one friend, and the food portions are referred to as mishloach manot (Hebrew for "sending of portions"). The custom has developed into sending gifts to many family members and friends, though only one is required, to show friendship and rejoicing. In addition, charity is given to at least two poor people.

On Purim day, towards evening, a festive meal called Seudat Purim is held. Wine is the main beverage, with drunkenness common, in remembrance of the feast of the King of Persia, where the evil Haman was miraculously sentenced to death by the king, with the subsequent deliverance of the entire Jewish people.

## Pesach (Passover)

The Festival of Pesach (Passover) occurs in the spring on the 15th of the Hebrew month of Nissan until the 21st or 22nd outside of Israel. It commemorates the liberation or Exodus of the Jews from Egyptian enslavement. The Bible relates that G-d inflicted ten plagues upon the Egyptians until their ruler, Pharaoh, agreed to release his Hebrew slaves, after the tenth plague killed every non-Jewish firstborn male, from Pharaoh's son to the firstborn cattle.

The Jews left in such a hurry that they had no time to allow their breads to rise. To commemorate this during Passover, no unleavened bread or food products are eaten or even kept in our possession, the bread being replaced with matzah. All leavened products are sold by the rabbi of the community to a non-Jew during the Passover holiday, so that they will not be in a Jew's possession during the holiday. A thorough cleaning and elimination of all leavened products, or storage of these products in specially marked cabinets or drawers occurs before the holiday in each house.

Many Jewish homes have separate dishes, pots, utensils, and stoves for use during Pesach or they use disposable tableware. Otherwise, special koshering procedures must be performed prior to Pesach each year. Counters and sinks are koshered and covered with heat impermeable materials. Prepared foods that are purchased must be labeled Kosher l'Pesach (Kosher for Pesach) backed by rabbinical supervision. A special unleavened wheat cracker-like bread, matzah, is eaten, and it is prepared commercially each year under strict rabbinical supervision.

Flour and grain, therefore, cannot be used during Pesach, since either may become naturally leavened quickly. A leavened product is referred to as chametz. Matzah, finely ground to form matzah meal is used by many in food preparation in place of flour. Sephardic Jews traditionally permit the use of legumes such as peas, chickpeas, and rice during Pesach.

The prohibition against eating leavened food products and regular flour during Passover results in increased use of matzah, potato, eggs, and oil. Meat, chicken, and fish are also commonly eaten in larger than usual amounts. Many Jews use milk and milk products specially supervised kosher l'Pesach, as well. While "Kosher for Passover" packaged goods are available, many families choose a stricter course, cooking everything at home during the week of Passover.

## The Passover Seder

The seder meal is a celebration feast that occurs on the evening of the first day of Pesach with many symbolic commemorations of our liberation from Egyptian bondage. Outside of the Land of Israel, the seder is repeated the second night of Pesach, as well.

It is traditional for Jewish families to gather for this special meal. The word seder is Hebrew for "order," and it refers to the special order of this ritual. During the meal the story of the Exodus from Egypt is retold in detail, using a special text, the Haggadah. A total of four cups of kosher wine or grape juice are taken by both men and women throughout the narrative. The seder is full of questions and answers and unusual practices to arouse questions and to keep the interest of the children, since this is truly a family event.

The children are rewarded with nuts, and they compete in a search for the afikoman, the piece of matzah which is the last item eaten at the seder. The conversation lasts well into the night with discussion, eating, and singing.

Maror, Hebrew for "bitter herbs," are eaten during the seder to remember the bitterness of Egyptian slavery. The maror is traditionally horseradish or romaine lettuce.

The seder is traditionally ended with a prayer that concludes, "Next year in Jerusalem!"

## Shavuot – The Festival of Weeks

Shavuot (or Shavuos in Ashkenazic pronunciation) is Hebrew for "weeks," and it is also known as the "Festival of Weeks." The holiday is fixed seven weeks after the second day of Passover on the 6th of the Hebrew month of Sivan (until the 7th of Sivan outside of Israel). Shavuot commemorates the anniversary of the day that G-d gave the Ten Commandments and the Torah to Moses and to the entire Hebrew nation at Mount Sinai seven weeks after their escape from Egyptian bondage. Shavuot is connected to the grain harvest in Israel. Harvesting of the barley began on Passover, and the harvesting of wheat at Shavuot, and the eighth day of Sukkot was the festival of the fruit harvest. Shavuot was also the first day that one could bring the bikkurim or first fruits of harvest to the ancient Temple in Jerusalem. The bikkurim were brought from the Seven Species for which the Land of Israel is praised: wheat, barley, grapes, figs, pomegranates, olives, and dates, which are more fully discussed in Chapter 6.

Dairy foods are traditionally served on Shavuot. Since the Jews had not yet received the Torah with its laws of ritual slaughtering (shechita), they decided to first eat dairy foods to honor the occasion. Cheesecake and cheese wrapped in dough, known as blintzes or kreplach in Yiddish, as spoken by many Ashkenazic Jews, are commonly served.

## Tisha B'Av

The 9th of the Hebrew month of Av, or in Hebrew Tisha b'Av, marks the destruction of both the First and Second of the ancient Temples of Jerusalem, and the beginning of the Jewish exile from the Holy Land of Israel. As a sign of mourning, Jews fast all day. For nine days preceding Tisha b'Av, meat and wine are not consumed, in remembrance of the destruction.

# A Summary of Jewish Holidays and Their Foods

**Rosh Hashana** – 1st and 2nd of Tishrei
> Jewish New Year
> Apples with honey, round challah breads, head of fish, carrot tzimmes, honey cake

**Yom Kippur** – 10th of Tishrei
> Day of Atonement
> Fast all day

**Sukkot** – 15th to the 22nd of Tishrei; until 23rd of Tishrei outside of Israel
> Festival of Booths (in which the Jews lived during the flight from Egypt)
> Kreplach or holishkes (chopped meat rolled in cabbage leaves), strudel

**Hanukah** – 25th of Kislev until the 2nd of Tevet
> Festival of Lights (battle of the Maccabees for Jewish independence)
> Oily and fried foods, grated potato latkes, jelly doughnuts, dairy foods

**Tu b'Shevat** – 15th of Shevat
> New Year of Trees (blossoming time in Israel)
> Fresh and dried fruits, nuts

**Purim** – 14th of Adar; 15th of Adar in Jerusalem known as Shushan Purim
> Feast of Esther (signifies the fall of Haman)
> Wine, Hamentashen (a three-cornered cookie filled with poppy seed)

**Pesach (Passover)** – 15th of Nissan until the 21st of Nissan (until 22nd of Nissan outside of Israel)
> Festival of Freedom (escape of the Jews from Egyptian slavery)
> Matzah, wine, romaine lettuce, horseradish; seder meal with other symbolic foods

**Shavuot** – 6th of Sivan until 7th of Sivan outside of Israel
> Festival of Weeks (Moses received the Ten Commandments and the Torah at Mount Sinai)
> Dairy foods, cheese blintzes, and cheese kreplach

**Tisha b'Av** – 9th of Av
> The day of destruction of both the 1st and 2nd Temples of Jerusalem
> Fast all day
> No meat or wine for nine days preceding

*Note: Jewish holidays always begin with the evening before the day listed.*

# Section II


# The Spirituality of Eating

# Chapter 4

# It All Began in the Garden

## SPIRITUALITY OF EATING

### Why Do We Eat?

When asked why they eat, people usually respond, "I eat because I'm hungry," "I eat when something looks or smells good," or "I eat because it's meal time." For many, the routine of eating is so boring or upsetting, they avoid or minimize it by skipping meals or using instant powders or fast foods. Others snack through the day without ever sitting down to a meal. In this chapter, we shall examine what really happens when we eat – from both spiritual and physical points of view.

### In The Beginning

To achieve historical perspective, we must go back in time to the beginning, to the Garden of Eden and the Tree of Knowledge.

> G-d took the man and put him into the Garden of Eden to work it and keep it. G-d commanded the man, saying, "You may freely eat from every tree of the garden. But from the Tree of Knowledge of Good and Evil do not eat, for on the day you eat from it, you will surely die. [*Genesis* 2:15-17]

If only the first man, Adam, had kept on occupying himself with G-d's commandments and with guarding the way to the Tree of Life, he would have continued to stroll through the Garden of Eden like one of the guardian angels! Shortly after G-d created Eve (Chava), in the afternoon of the first Friday of Creation, the first couple in the world committed the first sin by eating the forbidden fruit of the Tree of Knowledge of Good and Evil. If they had only waited a few hours for the Sabbath, they could have eaten the fruit with G-d's blessings, since Sabbath eating is on such a high spiritual level. [*Shaar ha-Kavaanos*, Rosh Hashanah, Discourse A]

Likewise, we read in the Chumash (Bible):

> The woman saw that the tree was good for food and
> desirable to the eyes, and the tree was attractive as a means
> to gain intelligence. She took some of its fruit and ate, and
> also gave some to her husband, and he ate. [*Genesis* 3:6]

The trees were real trees, the fruits were real fruits, and the eating was actual eating; but the fruits were fine and the eating was delicate. As the Ramchal (Rabbi Moshe Chayim Luzzatto) explains in *Da'as Tevunos*, the eating from the Tree of Knowledge introduced desire for all material, bodily pleasures, and for all sins.

In the beginning, good and evil had been separate, both in the fruit and in the entire world. But when the sin of the Tree of Knowledge corrupted the world, good became mixed with evil. Sparks of holiness fell into their husks, and the pure combined with the impure. Man was sentenced to work hard for his food and to eventually die. The world became more coarse and unrefined.

*The author is grateful to "Shamir" (the Association of Religious Professionals from The Soviet Union and Eastern Europe in Israel), which originally published this chapter in its publication *B'Or HaTorah* (no.8, 1993).

**Eat with Caution**

In *Tanna d'Vei Eliyahu*, the prophet Elijah acrimoniously blames all our troubles on eating:

> I call heaven and earth to bear witness that all the children of man are gathered to death and all creatures descend to sorrow only because of eating and drinking. [*Eliyahu Zuta* 3]

The commentary *Zikkukin d'Nura* explains that all sins result from overindulging in food and drink. We learn in the Torah that satiation leads to forgetting G-d or even rejecting G-d.

> You may eat and be satisfied...But your heart might grow haughty, and you might forget your G-d, Who brought you out of Egypt, the house of slavery. [*Deuteronomy* 8:12-14]

> For this reason we are commanded not to eat on Yom Kippur, the day of atonement for our sins, since improper eating has the power to turn our souls to wrongdoing. [Rabbenu Bachya, *Shulchan shel Arba'ah*]

**Hunger and Appetite Mechanisms**

Hunger is defined as an uneasy sensation caused by want of food. Appetite is the complex of sensations by which an organism is aware of its desire for food. The physical basis of hunger is regulated by the "feeding center" in the hypothalamic portion of the brain. The appetite-regulating mechanism in a normal human being adjusts food intake to the point where caloric intake balances the output of energy. This maintains body weight.

Thirst, the desire to drink, is regulated by the hypothalamic osmoreceptors of the brain. A dry sensation in the mouth also motivates a person to drink.

The physical basis of hunger and thirst has been well proven. However, the psychological motivating factors are often the overriding influence driving one to eat or drink too much or too little. Most habitual eating is unrelated to hunger. It is more related to one's surroundings, including the presence or reminders of food, or to one's emotional state. In short, we often eat for many reasons besides that of satisfying our physical need for food!

## COMPONENTS OF FOOD

It is clear that the soul is not nourished by physical bread, as the body is. The food we eat is actually a combination of both a physical and a spiritual entity. The body is nourished by the physical aspects – or nutrients – contained in the foods we eat. While the soul is nourished by the spiritual power – or sparks of holiness – which enlivens the physical substance of all matter, including food. Therefore, body and soul are united in the act of eating. [*Ruach Chayim* on *Pirkei Avos* 3:3; Shulchan Aruch, Orach Chaim 6:1, and see *Magen Avraham* verse 4]

We have seen that all of Creation is composed of a mixture of good and evil. Likewise, in every food that a person eats, there is a combination of good and evil. Food physically consists of good counterparts (i.e., nutrients), and bad aspects (i.e., waste or toxins). Likewise, spiritually, food contains sparks of holiness, or good components, and husks, or kelipos, which are the gross, bad components that encompass the sparks.

### Physical Origins: The Nutrients

Where does food come from? Plants grow by effectively combining sunlight, water, and nutrients from soil. Animals feed on plants and/or other animals. Humans obtain their food from mineral, plant, and animal sources.

Nutrients, which are contained in our food, must be consumed in adequate amounts in order for us to grow. In the body, these nutrients are broken down to or converted into thousands of substances, which contribute to healthy living.

Nutrients are divided into six general classes: carbohydrates, fats, proteins, vitamins, minerals, and water.

### Spiritual Origins: The Sparks – Shechina, Manna, Food

Before descending into the body, the soul is nourished as the angels are – directly through the radiance of the Shechina (the Divine Presence). The soul, separated by the body from its former supernal nourishment, is now nourished by physical food (which is the manifestation of that Divine nourishment). Thus, when one eats, one benefits somewhat from the radiance of the Shechina. [*Reshis Chachmah*, Sha'ar ha-Kedushah 15:51; *Siddur Tefillah l'Moshe*, edited by the Ramak]

> The soul, clothed in the physical garment of the flesh, is now nourished indirectly by G-d through food. Such is G-d's Will, that we should exist with our physical limitations, and that we should require physical food to sustain our vital forces. Only in the future world, when stripped of its physical garment, will food become recognizable as radiance of the Divine Presence. However, in this world it appears clothed in its physical garment. [*Peri Tzaddik,* Es ha-Ochel]

> Food, then, comes into the world from the supernal table of Heaven. [*Reshis Chachma,* Sha'ar ha-Kedushah 15:46]

> …The sin of eating from the Tree of Knowledge caused good to become mixed with evil throughout the world and sparks of holiness to fall amidst the husks. These sparks of holiness are scattered throughout Creation and are contained in varying amounts in the food we eat. These sparks of holiness give plants the strength to emerge and grow from the soil as they are watered by the rains. [*Yesod v'Shoresh ha-Avodah,* sha'ar 7, ch. 1]

After the Jews were redeemed from slavery in Egypt, they ate manna in the desert. Manna is not ordinary coarse food but, rather, a physical form of supernal light. It descended daily and, unlike all other foods, was completely absorbed into the body when eaten.

> ...In the morning, there was a layer of dew around the camp. When the layer of dew evaporated, the desert was covered with flakes like fine frost on the ground. The Israelites saw it and asked one another, "What is it?" (Man hu? in Hebrew) because they didn't know what it was, and Moses said to them, "This is the bread that G-d has given you to eat. [*Exodus* 16:13-15]

> The House of Israel called it manna (man in Hebrew). It looked like coriander seed except that it was white. It tasted like a honey wafer. [*Exodus* 16:31]

> Manna descended from Heaven completely good, with no mixture of evil, since no evil descends from Heaven. Therefore, it contained no waste and was absorbed completely. [*Ruach Chayim* on *Pirkei Avos* 3]

> The manna and the fruits of the Garden of Eden were similar in that they were both completely absorbed into the limbs of the body. [Ramban, *Genesis* 2:17]

| Combination of Good and Evil in Our Foods | | |
|---|---|---|
| | Spiritual Aspects | Physical Aspects |
| | (Soul) | (Body) |
| GOOD | Sparks | Nutrients |
| EVIL | Husks | Waste |

### Digestion of Food

Food is first introduced into the mouth, where it is chewed by the teeth in order to break up large food particles to mix it with saliva, thus beginning the process known as digestion. The food is then propelled into the esophagus by the tongue with the aid of the swallowing mechanism.

The food travels down the esophagus until it reaches the stomach. Food is stored in the stomach, mixed with acid, and other digestive juices, and released at a controlled, steady rate into the entrance of the small intestine, where it is digested further and absorbed. In the small intestine, the intestinal contents are mixed with pancreatic juice, bile, and other secretions.

The intestinal contents continue down the long, winding tube of the small intestine until they pass into the thick tube of the large intestine, the main function of which is to absorb water, salt and other minerals, and certain vitamins. Stool containing inorganic (non-carbon-containing) material, undigested plant fibers, bacteria, and water is excreted from the body through the rectum.

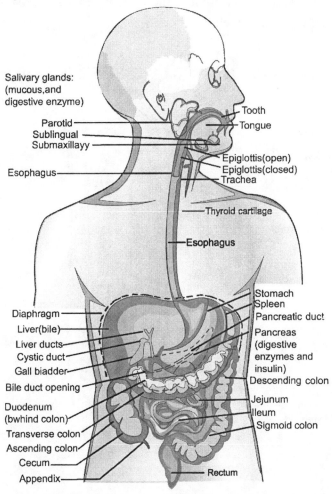

## Absorption of Food

Although limited amounts of water, alcohol, simple salts, and glucose are absorbed through the stomach wall, the small intestine is by far the most important organ for absorption. Absorption into the small intestine consists primarily of the transfer of nutrients from the interior (lumen) of the small intestine through the cells lining the intestinal wall into the wall of the small intestine (the lamina propria). From there the nutrients enter the blood and lymph vessels. The nutrients are then carried to all parts of the body through the bloodstream. The waste materials are eliminated from the body via stool, urine, sweat, and expired air. The small intestine, then, is the main site of selection of the nutrients for use in the body, leaving the waste for eventual elimination.

## CROSS SECTION OF VILLI AND LAYERS OF SMALL INTESTINES

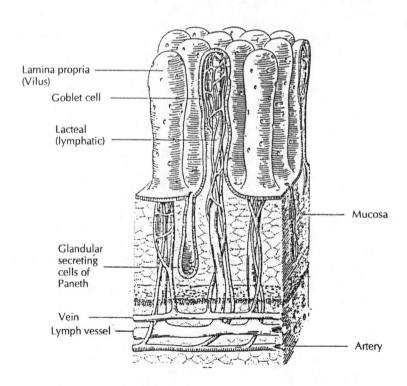

**Use of the Nutrients**

The end products of the digestive processes are amino acids from proteins, plus fat derivatives, and simple carbohydrates. These compounds are absorbed and metabolized in the body by various routes. The intricate details of their metabolism are studied by biochemists.

How do we get energy from the food we eat? The derivation of energy from a physical source is the most spiritual of our bodily processes. To function properly, the body must be constantly supplied with fuel or energy from either digesting food or drawing on its fat stores when adequate food is not available. The body's chemical energy is held in the high-energy bonds of adenosine triphosphate (ATP).

Plants derive ATP from light energy when they produce and store excess carbohydrates, mostly as starch. Through the food chain, the stored energy of plants becomes the potential energy of animals and man. Through their metabolic processes, animals and man convert stored plant energy into a usable form of ATP to sustain their life processes. Most of the energy consumed as food is used up as heat, released either directly in the body's metabolic reactions or as a by-product of work performed by the body. Only that part of food energy, which is captured in chemical form in the high-energy bonds of ATP can support these functions.

**The Spiritual Act of Eating: Releasing of the Sparks**

> ...Man does not live by bread alone, but by all that comes
> out of G-d's mouth. [*Deuteronomy* 8:3]

The separation of nutrients from waste in the act of eating has its spiritual counterpart in the extraction of the sparks of holiness, which are contained in food. And is not the physical and spiritual separation of good from evil the very meaning of human existence?

> When a person eats properly, with the right intention, the
> sparks of holiness from his food attach to his soul, and the waste
> is forced away. [*Yesod v'Shoresh hs-Avodah*, sha'ar 7, ch. 1]

The taste and pleasure that one experiences from food are actually not physical but are derived from the sparks of holiness contained in the food. Not all foods contain an equal amount of sparks and therefore (different foods) are not equal in taste. In general, the less tasty plants contain fewer sparks of holiness, and the even tastier animal foods contain the most sparks of holiness. The main energy that a person receives from his food comes from the sparks of holiness contained in the food, which attach themselves to his soul after eating. [*Yesod v'Shoresh ha-Avodah,* sha'ar 7, ch. 2]

## Blessings and Intention

A Jew does not gain true benefit from food without first blessing his Creator. After eating, he further blesses G-d for sustaining him.

We have already discussed the danger of forgetting G-d when we are satisfied. G-d has commanded medicine to be taken for this malady precisely at the dangerous moment when we are the most satisfied – to remember Him through the blessings after food. [Rabbenu Bachya, *Shulchan shel Arba'ah*]

When you have eaten and become satisfied, then you must bless the L-rd your G-d for the good land which He has given you. [*Deuteronomy* 8:10]

In this world, G-d's vitalizing force can only come to us clothed in the garment of food...In blessing his food a person shows his recognition of G-d's vitalizing force and his belief that G-d's Word is the essential element hidden within the food that he is now eating. [*Peri Tzaddik,* Es ha-Ochel]

While eating, if one recognizes that G-d has created and enlivened his food, has provided him with food, and furthermore has added taste to its beneficial elements – taste which arouses desire to increase strength and vitality – then even the pleasure he experiences from eating is purified and sanctified as a sacrifice of the altar. [*Peri Tzaddik,* Es ha-Ochel]

Another aspect of eating is the importance of learning Torah at the table, as our Sages have repeatedly emphasized.

> Rabbi Shimon said, "If three ate at the same table and did not utter words of Torah, it is as if they had partaken of an idolatrous meal." [*Pirkei Avos* 3:3]

## EATING IN JEWISH LAW AND TRADITION

Discussions on eating in Jewish law are found in tractate, subdivision, *Berachos* of the Talmud and in the Orach Chayim section of the book, *Shulchan Aruch*. Details on permitted and forbidden foods are found in the Yoreh De'ah section of the *Shulchan Aruch*. Agricultural restrictions on hybridization in the sabbatical year, and in the first three years after the planting of fruit trees are found respectively in the tractates *Kelayim, Shevi'is,* and *Orlah*. Food preparation on the Sabbath is discussed in tractate *Shabbos*; on festivals in tractate *Beitzah*; and on Pesach (Passover) in tractate *Pesachim*. In addition, in the *Abridged Shulchan Aruch*, ch. 32, there is a concise review of proper eating and health. The Rambam is the main source of discussion on health and eating in Jewish law (see his *Mishneh Torah*, Hilchos De'os, ch. 4).

### The Effects of Eating

Eating is one of our most common activities. It must be G-d's Will that we are so involved in eating. There must be an important spiritual purpose to it. If we really can separate good from evil by eating correctly, then this purification has great ramifications upon all levels of reality.

> G-d made this world one of choice and free will so that we should choose good and abhor evil. Therefore, sparks of holiness fell into this world, and good and evil were mixed. Man's main service to G-d is to gather and raise them up to the level from which the soul has been quarried. [*Mor v'Shemesh* on Parshas Pinchas]

Moreover, even one's special craving for or aversion to a particular food can be seen as a special sign that G-d has brought him food that needs rectification. [*Shulchan ha-Tahor*, Atsmus ha-Achillah, ch.6]

When one eats, the holy sparks [of the food] cleave to his soul. By blessing with the right intention before eating and by eating for the sake of Heaven, righteous people purify and raise up the sparks of holiness contained in the food they eat. When a person learns Torah, prays to G-d, or uses the strength obtained from food to perform a commandment, he elevates the sparks of holiness to the sanctified worlds of Heaven, whence they had originally fallen. The sparks of holiness are thereby returned to their source. [*Yesod v'Shoresh ha-Avodah*, sha'ar 7, chs. 1-2]

## Atonement of Sins – Holiness

Rabbi Yochanan and Rabbi Elazar said, "As long as the Temple stood, the sacrificial altar atoned for Israel; now a man's table atones for him." [*Berachos* 55a]

In other words, the table upon which we eat, is now our sacrificial altar; our food is our sacrifice; and we, through eating, offer the sacrifice in place of the Temple priest. [*Kol Menachem*] Our bodies metabolize this food and thereby release the nutrients and sparks.

During the times of our Temple in Jerusalem, a chief effect of sacrificing was the elevation and purification of the sparks of holiness contained in the sacrifices. Now that we no longer have the Temple service, our prayers, and our eating must serve this function. [*Yesod v'Shoresh ha-Avodah*, sha'ar 7, ch. 1]

Our eating for this elevated purpose – for the sake of Heaven – can bring us to holiness and cleaving to G-d. [*Reshis Chachmah*, Sha'ar ha-Kedushah 3:2]

And it will come to pass, if you diligently obey My commandments which I command you this day, to love

the L-rd your G-d and to serve Him with all your heart
and with all your soul, then I will give rain for your land at
the due time, the early rain and the late rain, and you will
gather in your grain, your wine, and your oil.  And I will
give you grass in your fields for your cattle, so that you can
eat and be satisfied. [*Deuteronomy* 11: 13-15]

The rain falls from above and helps the earth send forth vegetation. Animals feed on the plants and other animals; and, by serving G-d, man raises mineral, vegetable, and animal matter up to its source. When all the sparks of holiness are raised and returned to their source in Heaven, the way will be prepared for the Mashiach (Messiah) to come, we believe soon in our days.

## FESTIVAL OF THE TREES

...Then all the trees of the forest will sing for joy. [*Psalms* 96:12]

### Tu b'Shevat and the Renewal of Life

Tu b'Shevat, the fifteenth day of the Hebrew month of Shevat, marks the yearly beginning of the re-growth of the fruit of trees. This special day, known as the New Year of the Trees, signifies the time that most of the rainy season has passed in the Land of Israel, the time when the sap begins to rise in the tree trunks and the fruit trees begin to bud. [Rashi, Talmud, *Rosh Hashana* 14a] We annually witness this welcoming of spring while still in the midst of winter.

Because of the holiness of the Land of Israel and its centrality to Jews, the seasonal changes there determine when this renewal of life is celebrated. As Jews throughout the world eat fruits on Tu b'Shevat to commemorate the New Year of the Trees in the Land of Israel, we think about the importance of our homeland. Also, we are motivated to study the religious agricultural laws that apply to the Land of Israel, such as shemittah, orlah, terumah, and ma'aser.

The New Year of the Trees is a time to meditate on the wonders of Creation, which are revealed to us through the renewal of life. Tu b'Shevat is a day that should stimulate us to recognize G-d's miracles, which abound in His world and to appreciate G-d's great kindness, as we witness new life being put into His creation each spring.

### The Halachic Origins of Tu b'Shevat

The exact date of the festival is a subject of controversy in the Talmud, Beis Shammai insisting on the first day of the Hebrew month of Shevat while Beis Hillel advocates the fifteenth day of the month. [*Rosh Hashana*, 2a] The ruling of Beis Hillel is now accepted.

It has become customary among Jews to celebrate the New Year of the Trees by eating fruits. This practice apparently originated in the Ashkenazic tradition as is cited in the Shulchan Aruch (the Code of Jewish Law). The commentary, *Magen Avraham*, says: "The Ashkenazic Jews have the custom of eating many types of fruit" on the fifteenth of Shevat.* [*Magen Avraham* 16 on Shulchan Aruch, Orach Chayim 131]

Traditional Sephardic Jews have developed an elaborate fruit ceremony which includes eating thirty fruits. This Seder Tu b'Shevat is accompanied by extensive words of Torah to commemorate the holiday. [Peri Etz Hadar]

A popular Tu b'Shevat custom is to ask G-d to bless us with a kosher citron during the following fall's Sukkot festival.

(*The source referred to is the *Tikkun Yissachar* (62:25), written by Yissachar Sussan, who was one of the great Sephardic rabbis of Tzefat during the time of Rabbi Yosef Karo, author of the Shulchan Aruch, and the great kabbalist Rabbi Yitzchak Luria, known as the Ari Ha-kadosh.)

**For Man Is a Tree of the Field**

> When thou shalt besiege a city a long time, in making
> war against it to take it, thou shalt not destroy its trees by
> forcing an axe against them; for thou may eat of them, and
> thou shalt not cut them down; for is the tree of the field
> a man, that it should be besieged by thee? [*Deuteronomy*
> 20:19]

> In many ways man and trees are related, and frequently are
> interdependent. We often rely on their fruit for food. We
> use their wood for shelter and various other needs. Their
> leaves provide us with shade and comfort. Trees, likewise,
> are affected by our actions, sometimes in an obvious
> manner and sometimes in a more subtle way. From the day
> that the Temple was destroyed the taste of the fruits has
> been removed. Rav Yossi says that even the fat of the fruit
> has been removed. [*Sotah* 48a]

> Fruit and grain rot only because of the ways of man.
> [*Tanna d'Vei Eliyahu, Zuta* 3]

There are many similarities between men and trees. Both live off the
earth. Trees send down roots to draw sustenance from the soil. Likewise,
our food has its origin in the soil that supports the growth of the plants we
eat. The animals we eat are themselves nourished from the soil's vegetation. We both take in air, water, and nutrients, which are essential to our
survival, and both thrive in sunlight. We both produce fruit containing the
seeds of the upcoming generations.

Man's body and the tree's trunk are, respectively, their main structural
components. Our skin and its bark protect each from harm by outside
invaders. Our garments and its leaves protect each and give us our charac-
teristic appearances.

We can learn from trees and their fruit many wonderful insights that can deepen our service to G-d. David, king of Israel, inspires us and opens our hearts with psalms that often draw a parallel between man and tree:

> And he shall be like a tree planted by streams of water that brings forth its fruit in its season; its leaf also shall not wither; and in whatever he does he shall prosper. [*Psalms* 1:3]

> The righteous man flourishes like the palm tree; he grows like a cedar in the Lebanon. Those that are planted in the house of the L-rd shall flourish in the courts of our G-d. They still bring forth fruit in old age... [*Psalms* 92:13-15]

**In the Fruit Garden**

As do many discussions on the spiritual effects of eating, ours too returns – for perspective – to the primeval setting of the Garden of Eden and the Tree of Knowledge.

In the beginning, Adam was nourished solely by the fruits of the trees. The Garden of Eden was a luscious fruit garden that provided all of man's physical and spiritual needs. The fragrant garden was filled with trees, all blossoming with rich fruit. In the center of the garden were the two special trees, the Tree of Life and the Tree of Knowledge. These were surrounded by all the other fruit-bearing trees.

These precious, all-nourishing fruits were reserved for humans only, whereas the animals ate simple grasses and field herbs. [*Peri Tzaddik*, Tu b'Shevat]

G-d created man in such a manner that he must eat to live, and his nourishment was originally taken in holiness, according to G-d's instructions. In the beginning, G-d's sole positive commandment to man involved eating the fruit of the Garden of Eden.

> And the L-rd G-d commanded man, saying: "From all the trees of the garden you may surely eat." [*Genesis* 2:16]

Similarly, the sole negative commandment was the prohibition against eating forbidden fruit.

> And from the Tree of Knowledge of Good And Evil you
> shall not eat, since on the day you eat from it you will
> surely die. [*Genesis* 2:17]

Man lived in a paradise surrounded by fruit trees; and his subsistence from these trees was effortless. The trees brought forth their fruits, and even fully-prepared cakes, all for man's delight and sustenance. However, darkness descended when the first couple in the world committed the first sin by eating of the forbidden fruit of the Tree of Knowledge, as a result of the seductive words of the serpent. This act caused a combination of good and evil throughout the world; it caused many changes in what and how man eats; and it even caused changes in the trees themselves. Many trees ceased to bear fruit completely. In the other trees, most of the nourishing components or nutrients left the fruit, forcing man to expand his food sources in order to receive adequate nourishment. From the time of Adam and Eve's sin of eating from the Tree of Knowledge, there has been a need for spiritual rectification of food through eating. The act of eating in a holy way, by reciting the proper blessings, by eating kosher food, and by intending to use the energy obtained from the food eaten to serve G-d, physically and spiritually separates the good from the evil in the food. On the other hand, all the unrighteous behavior on the part of man throughout the generations has had a continuous degrading effect on the quality of the world's fruits. [*Chesed l'Avraham* 19]

Rabbi Yehoshua ben Levi explains in the Talmud that after Adam sinned by eating from the Tree of Knowledge, G-d told him that thereafter he would eat from the herbs of the field. [*Pesachim* 118a] Adam's eyes filled with tears as he asked: "Master of the universe, my donkey and I will eat from the same feed bag?" as previously herbs were eaten by animals and not by man. G-d then answered sternly: "By the sweat of your brow you will eat bread..." Unlike the grazing and foraging animals, man was destined to work hard for his living and would have to prepare his own food. From that day on the fruits, as well, were cursed and lost their position as the sole sustainers of human life.

*Antioxidants – A Hint of Days of Glory*

Having forfeited their role as the only source of nutrition for mankind – as reflected by the fact that their present nutritional composition is relatively minor – nevertheless, we do find small amounts of certain important chemicals in fruits, which hint at their glorious past and promising future.

Natural phytochemicals, known as antioxidants, are powerful cancer preventers found commonly in fruits. These protective factors help the plants themselves fight invading infections, which threaten their very existence. Researchers and nutritionists today have evidence that these same substances can fight cancerous cells in humans. Likewise, antioxidants are thought to have a role in the prevention of heart disease.

When the cells of our body use oxygen, they make by-products called free radicals. These free radicals may start chain reactions, which damage cells and thereby damage our health. Free radicals may also occur as a result of environmental factors such as pollution, sunlight, strenuous exercise, smoking, and radiation. Oxidative damage from free radicals may contribute to many common illnesses such as heart disease[1-3], diabetes [4,5], and cancer.[6]

Antioxidants, naturally present in many of our foods, can often prevent, repair, or at least slow down this damage. Antioxidants also improve immune defense and thereby lower the rate of infection.

Antioxidants are commonly found in foods such as beans and legumes, whole grains, fruits, and vegetables. These foods are all emphasized in our system of Jewish Natural Nutrition and will be discussed in Chapter 6 when we discuss the Seven Species of the Land of Israel, and in Chapter 12, when we summarize the Guidelines for Jewish Natural Nutrition.

Antioxidant nutrients found in foods include beta-carotene, vitamin A, vitamin E, vitamin C, selenium, lycopene, lutein, flavonoids, polyphenols, lignin and many others.

A summary list of some food sources of these antioxidant nutrients follows:

| Antioxidant | Food Sources |
| --- | --- |
| Beta-Carotene and Vitamin A | Mango, papaya, cantaloupe, pumpkin, peppers, spinach, apricots, carrots, broccoli, sweet potato, peaches, oranges, tomato, squash |
| Vitamin C | Oranges, grapefruit, melons, tomatoes, strawberries, green and raw peppers, kiwifruit, raw cabbage |
| Vitamin E | Vegetable oils, walnuts, peanuts, almonds, seeds, olives, avocado, wheat germ, whole grains |
| Selenium | Whole wheat bread, brown rice, Brazil nuts, chicken, red meat, eggs |
| Lycopene | Tomato sauce, ripe red tomatoes |
| Lutein | Spinach, kiwifruit, red peppers, kale, broccoli, Brussels sprouts |
| Lignin | Flax seeds, sunflower seeds, oatmeal, barley, rye |
| Flavonoids-Polyphenols | Grapes, red wine, pomegranate, blueberries, strawberries, cherries, apples, grapefruit, cranberries,  raspberries, blackberries, tea, walnuts, olives, chocolate |

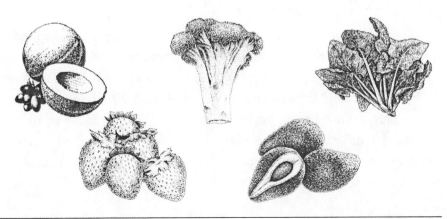

## NUTRITION IN THE END OF DAYS

In the Land of Israel every seven years the land is proclaimed "sanctified to G-d." The Torah forbids us to work our fields for profit, and instructs us to abandon crops. The seventh or sabbatical year, known as shemittah, teaches us to have faith in G-d to supply our needs, even at this time when we do not work the land. We learn to see G-d's hand in Creation, and we look forward to the Final Redemption, when G-d's complete control over His beautiful world will be revealed.

The Hebrew month of Shevat, like the shemittah year, reminds us of G-d's Creation of the world and of the Final Redemption, as the dry, withered trees of winter begin to show new life and vitality. The month of Shevat heralds the approach of Purim and Pesach (Passover), holidays of joy and redemption. Shevat also is a time for the rectification of improper eating, preparatory to the Purim holiday meal and the eating of matzah (unleavened bread) and bitter herbs on Pesach. [*Peri Tzaddik*, Tu b'Shevat 35] According to Beis Shammai, this spiritual work begins on the very first day of the month of Shevat.

The special day of Tu b'Shevat reminds us of the importance of rectifying the sin of eating from the Tree of Knowledge. By this rectification we hasten the ultimate Redemption. We recite the blessing over fruit before eating, to add to its holiness. We hope that proper eating on our part will affect the fruit trees as well as ourselves, restoring us to the position we once held in the Garden of Eden. [Midrash, *Bereshis Rabbah* 12] As we eat the fruits of Tu b'Shevat, our soul yearns to reach the level of eating enjoyed by Adam before he sinned.

The Talmud relates the story of Rabbi Shimon bar Yochai, who fled from Roman persecution at the time of the destruction of the Second Temple in Jerusalem and hid with his son in a cave in the mountains. [Talmud, *Shabbos* 33b] Their sole source of food was the nearby carob tree, which sustained them for many years until they came out of hiding. This story reminds us of the special all-nourishing trees of the Garden of Eden. Perhaps it also hints at a future time when once again trees alone will be able to sustain human life.

In the World-to-Come, when the Mashiach (Messiah) has arrived, trees will regain the complete strength that they possessed in the Garden of Eden. The non-fruit bearing trees will all begin to bear fruit! As the Talmud states:

> Rabbi Chiya ben Ashi said in the name of Rav: "In future days, the non-fruit-bearing trees of Israel will be loaded down with fruits…" [Talmud, *Kesubbos* 112b]

> Then the trees will all sing G-d's praise [*Perek Shirah* 3], as King David predicted: "…Then all the trees of the forest will sing for joy." [*Psalms* 96:12]

All fruits will increase in size, taste, and beauty, especially those in the Land of Israel. [*Chesed l'Avraham* 19] According to Rabban Gamliel, these future trees will bear new fruit daily. The trees of the Land of Israel will, also produce fully-formed cakes, as they did at the beginning of Creation, and there will be no lack of food.  [Talmud, *Shabbos* 30b]

The Midrash adds that in the World-to-Come man will be ultimately healed by eating the fruits of the Garden of Eden. [Midrash, *Devarim Rabbah* 1:1 and *Shemos Rabbah* 15:21]

May it be G-d's Will that we should reach that destination where the trees will sing G-d's praise and nourish us and heal us completely.

# References

1.  Van Gaal L, Mertens I, De Block C. (2006) Mechanisms linking obesity with cardiovascular disease. *Nature.* 444 (7121): 875-80. Doi: 10.1038/nature 05487. PMID 17167476.

2.  Aviram M. (2000) Review of human studies on oxidative damage and antioxidant protection related to cardiovascular diseases. *Free Radic Res.* 33 Suppl: 585-97. PMID 111 91279.

3.  Stanner SA, Hughes J, Kelly CN, Buttriss J. (2004) A review of the epidemiological evidence for the antioxidant hypothesis. *Public Health Nutr.* 7 (3): 407-22. doi: 10.1079/PHN 2003543. PMID 15153272.

4.  Davi G, Falco A, Patrono C. (2005) Lipid peroxidation in diabetes mellitus. *Antioxid Redox Signal.* 7 (1-2): 256-68. doi: 10.1089/ars.2005.7.256. PMID 15650413.

5.  Giugliano D, Ceriello A, Paolisso G. (1996) Oxidative stress and diabetic vascular complications. *Diabetes Care.* 19 (3):257-69. doi: 10.2337/diacare. 19.3.257. PMID 8742574.

6.  Food, Nutrition, Physical Activity, and the Prevention of Cancer: a Global Perspective. *World Cancer Research Fund* (2007). ISBN 978-0-9722522-2-5.

# Chapter 5

## Kabbalah and The Tree of Life

### What Is Kabbalah?

Kabbalah are the teachings to explain the inner meaning of both the Bible and rabbinical literature, as well as to give insights into the significance of Jewish religious practices. The proper study of kabbalah affects the manner in which a Jew observes the commandments, and it influences one to live life on a deeper level of understanding.

The Hebrew word "sod," translated as "secret" or "mystery," refers to these inner, esoteric meanings, as expressed in the kabbalistic literature. This is in contrast to the simple or direction interpretations taught in the general Torah sources. These secrets have traditionally been kept hidden, so that an unworthy person will not study them. Although intelligence is required, it is not adequate, and righteousness and faithfulness to the Creator are prerequisites for progress in this area of study. The teachings are often quite abstract, and they can be easily misinterpreted. The term kabbalah is Hebrew for "receiving," and so G-d chooses whom He wishes to receive these insights, and to what degree.

Traditionally, kabbalah dates from Eden with the first text attributed to Adam, the first man, and given to him by the angel Azriel. The "Book of Formation" is attributed to the Patriarch Abraham. Kabbalistic knowledge is also believed to be a part of the Oral Law given by G-d to Moses on Mount Sinai, together with the Written Law.

The discussion of the Seven Species of the Land of Israel and their connection to the ten kabbalistic sefirot is presented in a separate chapter, and is an example of an insight according to Jewish mysticism.

Kabbalah, or Jewish mysticism, contains the inner-most teachings of the Torah. These are often referred to as the secrets or the esoteric parts of the Torah. The true secrets, the deepest hidden meanings, are known only to G-d. Jewish tradition teaches that what the human mind can conceive is only a mere fraction of the Infinite knowledge. Nevertheless, it takes intellect and imagination to grasp what G-d has allowed to be revealed in the secret writings. He allows only those who sanctify themselves in holiness and purity to truly grasp the secrets of the kabbalah.

Kabbalah can be divided into three parts: the practical, the meditative, and the theoretical. Practical kabbalah is the use of the secret names of G-d and amulets to evoke supernatural powers, which is not encouraged now, and it may be dangerous and spiritually degrading. (An amulet is an object that protects a person from trouble; these may include gems, statues, coins, drawings, rings, pendants, holy books, and other items.)

Few texts of the practical kabbalah have survived. The meditative kabbalah contains techniques used to enhance spiritual development and a cleaving to G-d, through a release from physicality.

Theoretical kabbalah provides an intellectual framework to explain the mysteries of the Torah. There are thousands of kabbalah texts in print, most of which deal with the theoretical teachings. The best known of these include the *Book of Splendor (Zohar)*, the *Book of Illumination (Bahir)*, the *Gates of Light*, the *Orchard of Pomegranates*, and the writings of the Ari.

The Patriarchs and the prophets used kabbalistic meditative techniques to achieve enlightenment and prophecy. During the First Century, from the early Talmudic period, some of the main kabbalah classics were written, including the *Book of Formation (Sefer Yetzirah)*, the *Bahir,* and the *Zohar.* The *Zohar*, one of the best-known kabbalistic texts, was published in the middle 1290's. It is attributed to the Second Century mystic, Rabbi Shimon bar Yochai, and it was published by Rabbi Moshe de Leon.

The *Gates of Light* (Sharei Orah) was written by the great kabbalist Rabbi Yosef Gikatalia (1248 C.E.-1323 C.E.). It describes in detail the attributes of the ten mystical spheres (sefirot in Hebrew) and the ten Divine Names that are associated with them.

The Ramak, Rabbi Moshe Cordevero (1522 C.E.-1570 C.E.) of Safed, Israel, was one of the greatest theoretical kabbalists. He systematized the teachings of kabbalah in his classic text, the *Orchard of Pomegranates* (*Pardes Rimonim*).

Rabbi Isaac Luria (1534 C.E.-1572 C.E.) of Safed, Israel, considered the greatest kabbalist of modern times, is known as the "holy Ari." His closest disciple, Rabbi Chaim Vital, was the author of the Ari's teachings, as expressed in many famous texts such as the *Tree of Life* (*Etz Chaim*) and *Fruit of the Tree of Life* (*Pri Etz Chaim*), as well as the *Eight Gates*.

**The Kabbalistic Tree of Life**

One of the better known concepts of kabbalistic thought involves the kabbalistic Tree of Life, represented as follows:

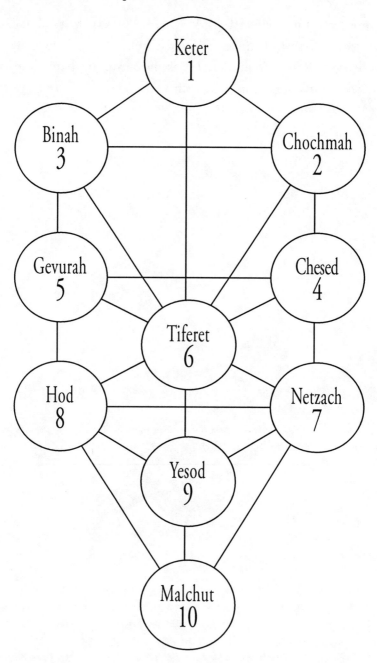

This is a mystical symbol used by the kabbalists, and it is a representation of a highly abstract, spiritual concept, and not a physical entity. It consists of the thirty-two "paths," combining the ten "sefirot" and the twenty-two paths through which they interrelate. It is a description of the path of Creation and of the mechanism through which G-d conducts His world, as represented by the sefirot.  It is important to remember that Jewish belief is that the sefirot are not separate aspects or emanations, and they do not separate the unity of G-d, nor do they act independently of G-d. They are manifestations of the Creator (the Infinite One), blessed be His Name, through which He conducts His world. Through the sefirot there is a revelation of the Infinite Light.

The names of the ten sefirot, as represented in the diagram, are listed, as follows:

1. Keter (Crown)
2. Chochmah (Wisdom)
3. Binah (Understanding)
4. Chesed (Love)
5. Gevurah (Strength)
6. Tiferet (Beauty)
7. Netzach (Victory)
8. Hod (Splendor)
9. Yesod (Foundation)
10. Malchut (Kingship)

Descriptions of the sefirot, how they interact, and how they reveal G-d's Will, are discussed in great detail in the kabbalistic texts.

# Chapter 6

# Seven Species of The Land of Israel

In the Bible, G-d shows His great love for the Land of Israel, by praising it as:

> ...a land of wheat, and barley, and vines (grapes), and fig trees, and pomegranates; a land of olive oil, and honey (dates). [*Deuteronomy* 8:8]

The foods mentioned above are known as the Seven Species (shivat ha-Minim) of the Land of Israel. They were of such value that they were the only products deemed worthy of being offered as the first fruits (bikkurim) in the Jerusalem Temple on Shavuot (Feast of Weeks). These first fruits were placed in baskets often woven with gold and silver. The baskets were then placed on oxen whose horns were plated with gold and whose heads were covered with crowns of olive branches. They were led to Jerusalem accompanied by music and rejoicing.

At the Temple each farmer would present his bikkurim to a priest (cohen) with a special ceremony. This ceremony of bikkurim shows the Jew's gratitude to G-d for the first fruits of the field, and for His guidance in general. The Midrash (commentary on the Bible) teaches us that, "In the merit of bikkurim the world was created." [Midrash, *Bereshis Rabbah* 1:6] It is no wonder, then, that the Seven Species of the Land of Israel are still so greatly treasured!

The Midrash also teaches us that in the World-to-Come, as we have learned previously, man will be ultimately healed by eating the fruits of the Garden of Eden. [Midrash, *Devarim Rabbah* 1:1 and *Shemos Rabbah* 15:21] Nutritionally, it is interesting to note that we can already find much disease-prevention and healing power in the grains and fruits of the Seven Species, hinting at a precursor of the healthy times to come.

Modern research is beginning to reveal many important healing aspects in each of these species, some of which will be briefly discussed, followed by a look into some of their deeper spiritual aspects.

## PHYSICAL ASPECTS OF THE SEVEN SPECIES OF THE LAND OF ISRAEL

### A Land of Wheat

Where there is no flour, there is no Torah. [Mishna, *Avos* 3:21]

Wheat is a very basic food, a universal symbol of eating. There is an opinion that the Tree of Knowledge was a wheat tree. [Midrash, *Rabbah, Bereshis* 15:7] Also, in the Garden of Eden wheat grew on trees, ready to eat as rich cakes. However, when Adam was cursed for his sin with "eating by the sweat of his brow," he began working hard to transform wheat to bread.

Wheat, in its natural, unrefined state has many important nutrients. The many health benefits of whole wheat products are recognized.[1] The popular Mediterranean diet approach to health emphasizes whole grains, whole wheat and barley, as well as the other components of the Seven Species.

Fiber, both insoluble and soluble, contained in whole wheat products are now considered health protective. They may help to maintain a healthy weight, reduce the risk of metabolic syndrome and insulin resistance (precursors to type 2 diabetes). The insoluble fiber in whole wheat has a laxative effect, and it may help prevent gallstones.

Research is beginning to show that whole grains, such as whole wheat, contain many powerful phytonutrients, whose activity has gone unrecognized. Plant lignans, abundant in whole wheat, are thought to protect against various forms of cancer, as well as heart disease.[1]

**Barley**

Barley was used in the counting of the omer from Passover to the Shavuos holiday during the times of the Jerusalem Temple.

The health benefits of barley are believed to include a decreased risk of cancer, heart disease, and type 2 diabetes.[2] It is believed that benefits from barley may be due to its content of beta-glucan, a soluble fiber. Benefits include reduction in total cholesterol and a stabilizing effect on blood sugar levels. There is evidence for a role in weight control, treatment of constipation, and in reduction of blood pressure.

**Grapes**

...and wine that gladdens the heart of man. [*Psalms* 104:15]

Grapes are the source of wine, our most sacred beverage. Wine is also a symbol of joy. Wine was poured on the Temple altar, and it is, until this day, used in many of our most sacred religious ceremonies.

Grapes are a source of several nutrients such as vitamins A, C, $B_6$, and folate. Perhaps more important, there are many disease-preventing components, as well.

Bioflavinoids functioning as antioxidants, together with resveratrol and caffeic acid, especially in red grapes, are important for cancer prevention. Polyphenols (an antioxidant), resveratrol, pterostilbene, and saponins are useful for preventing coronary heart disease.[3] Their high concentration of tannin may help fight viruses and tumors.

**Figs**

> He who guards the fig tree shall eat its fruit. [*Proverbs* 27:18]

The fig is first mentioned in the Torah when Adam and Eve covered their nakedness with fig leaves. [*Genesis* 3:7]

Besides its potassium and fiber content, figs are a good source of the trace mineral manganese, as well as of calcium and iron.[4-5] Fig leaves have been shown to have anti-diabetic properties.[4] In animal studies, fig leaves have been shown to lower triglyceride levels (a normal form of fat that circulates in the bloodstream). Some initial studies have shown inhibition of certain types of cancer growth.[5] Researchers have not yet determined which substances are responsible for these healing effects. This points out that much is still awaiting discovery with relation to the healing effects of the Seven Species.

**Pomegranate**

> Thy cheek is like a piece of a pomegranate within thy locks. [*Song of Songs* 4:3]

Jewish tradition teaches that the pomegranate is a symbol of righteousness, since it is said to have 613 seeds, which corresponds to the 613 mitzvot or commandments of the Torah. [Talmud, *Eruvin* 72]

Scientists in Israel have been studying the health benefits of pomegranates for years, and others have recently joined in. Researchers report that pomegranates are rich in antioxidants which prevent the bad LDL cholesterol from oxidizing, thus preventing atherosclerotic heart disease.[6,7] The fruit is now known to contain anti-carcinogenic, anti-atherosclerotic, anti-microbial and anti-viral compounds, due to its high antioxidant and polyphenol content.[6,7] Full health benefits from this wonderful fruit are just beginning to be realized.

**Olive**

> The L-rd called thy name, a green olive tree, fair with
> goodly fruit. [*Jeremiah* 11:16]

Olive oil was used to light the great *menorah* (lamp) in the ancient
Jerusalem Temple. It is rich in monounsaturated fat, a type of fat that is
known to have excellent health benefits. People who use olive oil regularly have much lower rates of heart disease, diabetes, and colon cancer.[8-10]
Recent studies show that olive oil contains much more that just monounsaturated fat. It is also rich in antioxidant and phenolic compounds with a
variety of protective benefits.[9] Antioxidants in olive oil include chlorophyll,
carotenoids and the polyphenolic compounds tyrosol, hydrotyrosol and
oleuropein, which also protect its vitamin E.[8,9]

**Dates**

> The righteous man flourishes like the palm tree. [*Psalms* 92:13]

"Honey" in the Seven Species refers to dates. Dates are the fruit of the
date palm tree. Being a laxative food, they have been found beneficial for
those suffering from constipation. Their nicotinic content is reported to
aid in intestinal disturbances. Regular consumption of dates may help in
the growth of friendly bacteria in the intestines.

## SPECIES OF THE LAND OF ISRAEL: UNDERSTANDING THEIR SPIRITUALITY

Why does G-d praise the Holy Land with grains and fruits? Why were there cakes growing on the trees in the Garden of Eden together with fruits? Wouldn't the Jewish people have been more excited to hear that the Land of Israel, which they were promised, was rich in cattle so they could eat some rich meat?

It becomes obvious that the foods of the Seven Species of the Land of Israel contain some of the mysteries of Creation! [*ha-Recanti*, Ekev] Contemplation of the spiritual aspects of the Seven Species increases one's understanding of the foods in the Garden of Eden and in the World-to-Come, and in general, of the spiritual source of foods. The manna included them all as the source of all foods, created by G-d just before the first Sabbath during the six days of Creation. [Mishna, *Avos* 5:9]

Putting all we have learned together, we see that there is a hierarchy of trees. The most exalted is represented as the Tree of Life, an apple tree, in the Garden of Eden. Then, there was the Tree of Knowledge of Good and Evil. The Midrash brings four opinions: wheat, grapes, citron, or fig as to what this tree was. [Midrash, *Rabbah Bereshis* 15:7] The Talmud speaks of just three possibilities: wheat, grapes, or figs. [Talmud, *Berachos* 40a; *Sanhedrin* 70a]

There were also many other trees in the Garden of Eden, all bearing either fruits or cakes, which will also be the case in the World-to-Come. Among these trees were included the grains and fruits of the Seven Species of the Land of Israel, wheat, barley, grapes, figs, pomegranates, olives and dates. The wheat and barley are chosen, but there are actually five species of grain, including oats, rye, and spelt, giving a total of five grain species. [Rabbenu Bachaya, Ekev 8] [*ha-Recanti*, Ekev] [Mishna, *Challah* 1] Together with the five species of fruits, this begins to explain why there were cakes from grains as well as fruits on the trees in the Garden of Eden, and as there will also be in the World-to-Come. The order of the foods listed in the scripture is spiritually significant, as are the choices of the foods, which shall be examined in the mystical context.

The five grains (the original wheat and barley, together with the additional implied three: oats, rye, and spelt) and the five fruits (grapes, figs, pomegranates, olives, and dates) are representative of the ten mystical sefirot, as taught in kabbalah. The Seven Species alone (without the top three – see page 72) represent the seven days of Creation or the lower seven mystical sefirot, and the seven Patriarchs, Abraham, Isaac, Jacob, Moses, Aaron, Joseph, and David.

One of the most important teachings of kabbalah, the mystical aspects of the Torah, involves the ten sefirot (or sefiros) (singular, sefirah) or Divine emanations. The ten sefirot are called keter (crown), chochmah (wisdom), binah (understanding), chesed (kindness, love), gevurah (strength, power), tiferet (beauty), netzach (victory), hod (splendor), yesod (foundation), and malchut (kingship). They are not entities that are distinct from their Emanator, which would imply plurality in G-d. No place or physicality should be attributed to the sefirot. It is through these attributes that G-d, so to speak, creates and conducts His universe. More in-depth discussion of the sefirot is beyond the scope of this text. Nevertheless, the reader should know that they exist, since this increases our understanding of the spiritual side of nutrition.

The Jewish mystics (kabbalists) were aware of a connection between the Seven Species and the sefirot. [Rabbi Chaim Vital, *Lekutai Torah*, Ekev] The diagram presented shows a schematic representation of the Species of the Land of Israel and their relationship to the ten sefirot. Note that the order of the species matches the order in scripture!

> ...a land of wheat, and barley, and vines (grapes), and fig trees, and pomegranates; a land of olive oil and honey (dates). [*Deuteronomy* 8:8]

# The Ten Sefirot and the Species of the Land of Israel

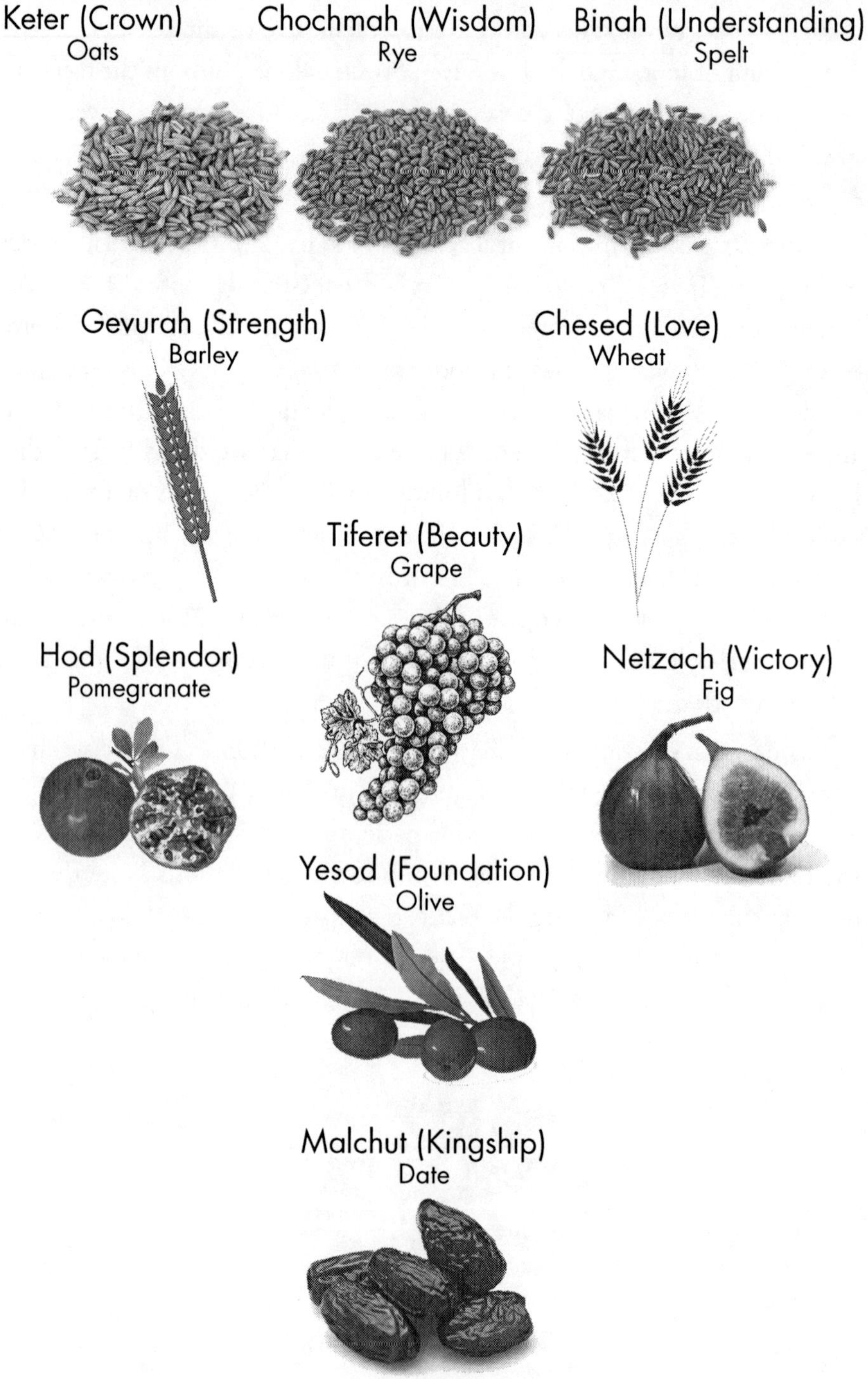

**Keter (Crown)**
Oats

**Chochmah (Wisdom)**
Rye

**Binah (Understanding)**
Spelt

**Gevurah (Strength)**
Barley

**Chesed (Love)**
Wheat

**Tiferet (Beauty)**
Grape

**Hod (Splendor)**
Pomegranate

**Netzach (Victory)**
Fig

**Yesod (Foundation)**
Olive

**Malchut (Kingship)**
Date

As we have seen, there are praises by G-d for the Seven Species through-out our holy scriptures. Their relationship to the ten mystical sefirot en-hances their importance, as they can be thought to be representative of all foods. The flow of supernal sustenance (shefa) comes down, so-to-speak, from G-d, the Infinite, through the Species of the Land of Israel (which figuratively represent the sefirot) to nourish the entire world, in His great kindness and mercy. [*ha-Recanti*, Ekev]

> When thou hast eaten and art replete, then thou shalt bless the L-rd thy G-d for the good land which He has given thee. [*Deuteronomy* 8:10]

> ... a land flowing with milk and honey. [*Exodus* 3:8]

# References

1.  Jensen MK, Koh-Banerjee P, Hu FB, Franz M, Sampson L, Gronbaek M, Rimm EB. Intakes of whole grains, bran, and germ and the risk of coronary heart disease in men, *Am J Clin Nutr.* 2004 Dec; 80(6): 1492-9, 2004 PMID: 15585760.

2.  Behall KM, Scholfield DJ, Hallfrisch J. Diets containing barley significantly reduce lipids in mildly hypercholesterolemic men and women. *Am J Clin Nutr.* Nov; 80 (5): 1185 – 93. 2004. PMID: 15531664.

3.  Dohadwala MM, Vita JA. Grapes and cardiovascular disease. *J Nutr.* 2009. Sep; 139 (9): 17885 – 935. 2009.

4.  Serraclara A, Hawkins F, Perez C, et. al. Hypoglycemic action of an oral fig-leaf decoction in type-I diabetic patients. *Diabetes Res Clin Pract.* 1998 Jan; 39 (1): 19–22. 1998. PMID: 13430.

5.  Rubnov S, Kashman Y, Rabinowitz R, et. al. Suppressors of cancer cell proliferation from fig (Ficus carica) resin: isolation and structure elucidation. *J Nat Prod.* 2001 Jul; 64 (7); 993 – 6. 2001. PMID:13390.

6.  Mertens-Talcott SU, Jilma-Stohlawetz P, Rios J, Hingorani L, Derendorf H. Absorption, metabolism, and antioxidant effects of pomegranate *(Punica granatum)* polyphenols after ingestion of a standardized extract in healthy human volunteers. *J Agric Food Chem.* 54 (23) Nov 2006; 8956 – 61. PMID: 17090147.

7.  Aviram M, Rosenblat M, Gaitini D, et. al.Pomegranate juice consumption for 3 years by patients with carotid artery stenosis reduces common carotid intima-media thickness, blood pressure and LDL oxidation, *Clin Nutr.* 23 (3), Jun 2004; 423 – 33, PMID: 15158307.

8.  Kontogianni MD, Panagiotakos DB, Chrysohoou C, et al. The impact of olive oil consumption pattern on the risk of acute coronary syndromes; The CARDIO 2000 case-control study. *Clin Cardiol.* 2007. Mar; 30 (3); 125–9. 2007. PMID: 17385704.

9.  Covas MI, Nyyssonen K, Poulsen HE, et al., EUROLIVE Study Group. The effect of polyphenols in olive oil on heart disease risk factors: a randomized trial. *Ann Intern Med.* 2006; Sept 5; 145 (5): 333–41. 2006. PMID:16954359.

10. Hashim YZ, Eng M, Gill CI, et al. Components of olive oil and chemoprevention of colorectal cancer. *Nutr Rev.* 2005 Nov; 63 (11): 374–86. 2005. PMID: 16370222.

# Chapter 7

# *The Apple: Symbol of Health*

You have entered the orchard of the tree of the holy apples. The sight of the beautiful, lush apple tree with its sweet-smelling fruit overwhelms you. It is a sight and fragrance that you have never before experienced. You stand in the Garden of Eden and gaze in amazement at your surroundings. In the background are many other fruit-bearing trees of various kinds. What is the inner meaning of the beautiful apple tree and its fruit? You are overwhelmed by a desire to know the full meaning of all that you are experiencing. It is clear that the apple tree and its fruit are not simple phenomena; nor are the other trees. They represent the essence of life on its deepest level.

## THE APPLE TREE: SYMBOL OF G-D

The Talmud, in *Ta'anis 5b*, compares G-d to a fruit tree. The story goes that a tired, hungry, and thirsty traveler passing through a desert, comes upon a tree whose fruit is sweet, whose shade is pleasant, and at whose base flows a stream. The traveler eats from the fruit, drinks from the water, and rests in the shade of the tree. When he rises to leave, he proclaims: "Tree, tree, how can I bless you? If I would say that you should have sweet fruit, you already have it; that your shade should be pleasant, it already is; that a stream of water should pass by you, you already have a passing stream. Therefore, may it be His Will that all your offspring should be as yourself."

In this parable, the stream represents the Torah, from which all those who thirst for the word of G-d may drink. The fruits are the children – the Jewish people – who, we pray, will grow in holiness, following the ways of the tree. And the tree clearly represents the Almighty, may His Name be blessed, Who is the paragon of perfection. We read in *Song of Songs* [2:3]:

> Like the apple tree among the trees of the forest, so is my
> Beloved among the sons. I sat down under His shadow
> with great delight, and His fruit was sweet to my taste.

Rashi explains that the apple tree represents G-d, Who is distinguished from the false gods.

The apple tree blossoms in the spring, in the month of Nissan, and its fruit ripens fifty days later, in the month of Sivan. This is likened to G-d's giving of the Torah: "He redeemed us from Egypt in Nissan, and after fifty days gave us His Torah." [*Shirha-Shirim Rabbah* 2] Having received the Torah, the Jewish people now sit, figuratively speaking, in the shade of G-d, protected by Him, and by His Torah.

The holy *Zohar* often praises G-d through the symbol of the apple:

> The apple is distinguished in color from all the trees.
> [*Zohar*, Ha'azinu]

> The apple's taste is sweet. [*Zohar*, Acharei Mos]

> The apple has a finer fragrance than all the other trees. [*ibid.*]

> The apple heals all. [*ibid.*]

All these references to apple mean G-d, Who is most exalted in His appearance, taste, fragrance, and healing ability.

Rabbi Tzaddok Ha-kohen explains that the Tree of Life refers to the Holy One, blessed be He, Who is called "the apple tree." [*Peri Tzaddik*, Shelach 52] This again, refers to the scripture, "Like the apple tree among the trees of the forest ..."

The tree, of course, is merely a symbol. Our limited minds obviously cannot comprehend the Infinite One. The apples of the tree are just representations of a spiritual phenomenon. The Torah speaks in terms that human minds can comprehend; it uses a physical sign to point to a spiritual reality. We are really talking about a spiritual tree that yields spiritual apples.

The main revelation of G-dliness and of the flow of life-giving vitality from Heaven is provided through the symbol of the Tree of Life, which also represents the Torah, and from there the vitality spreads to all the trees of the Garden of Eden, and on and on, to the entire Creation.

## THE SWEET APPLE: SYMBOL OF THE JEWISH PEOPLE

"… and its fruit was sweet to my taste." [*Song of Songs* 2:3]

The fruits of this special tree (which symbolizes G-d) are its offspring, the Jewish people, who are commanded by G-d to grow in the way of holiness, following the example of G-d and His holy Torah. Rabbi Tzaddok Ha-kohen explains that the fruits of the Tree of Life represent the souls of the righteous, which are like sweet fruit to G-d's palate. [*Peri Tzaddik*, Shelach 52]

We recall that when the Patriarch Jacob (Ya'akov) came to his father, Isaac (Yitzchak), to receive his blessing, Isaac sensed the aroma of Jacob's clothes and remarked, "My son's fragrance is like the fragrance of the field which is blessed by G-d." [*Genesis* 27:27] Rashi explains here that the sweet fragrance was that of the Garden of Eden, which entered with Jacob; the fragrance of the field blessed by G-d is the fragrance of the field of the holy apples.

In kabbalistic writings, the Friday night Sabbath meal also is referred to as "the field of the holy apples." That is the time when the Shechinah, G-d's Divine Presence, dwells among the Jewish people, when we receive the holiness of the entering Sabbath Queen. [*Peri Tzaddik*, Shemini Atzeres] It is at that special time that the Jewish people are called "holy apples." [*Peri Tzaddik*, Shelach 53]

The Ben Ish Chai also connects the apple to the field of the holy apples and the scripture "My son's fragrance is like the fragrance of the field …" He explains, further, that this is why we eat apples during the evening meals on Rosh Hashana, the Jewish New Year, since the apple is distinguished in three ways – taste, appearance, and fragrance – as we have mentioned previously. [*Halachos*, Nitzavim]  We eat apples as a sign that we will be blessed with children, life, and sustenance throughout the new year. [Shulchan Aruch, *Orach Chayim* 3, Hilchos Rosh Hashana, *Taz*]

The Talmud compares the Jewish people to the apple with regard to our receiving the Torah at Mt. Sinai. [Talmud, *Shabbos* 88a] Just as the blossoming of the apple tree precedes the formation of leaves, so the Jewish people agreed to perform the Torah's commandments even before hearing them. [Na'aseh v'nishma] Rashi explains that in most trees the leaves grow before the fruit blossoms. [Talmud, *Shabbos* 88a] Apple trees, however, blossom before they develop leaves. This process, specific to the apple tree, illustrates the unusual character of the Jewish people, who are ready to perform G-d's Will unconditionally.

The apple, ultimately, symbolizes our connection to G-d. We are likened to the apple just as G-d is compared to the apple tree. G-d expects us to live in holiness, just as He is holy. The Midrash presents the example of a king who married. [Midrash, *Tanchuma,* Kedoshim] The king explains to his new bride: "Since you married me and I am the king, you are therefore the queen; just as I am 'Your Royal Highness,' so you are 'Your Highness.'" Likewise, just as G-d is the King, so we, the Jewish people, are His queen, by association. In the same manner, the apples, i.e., the Jewish people, are attached to the apple tree, G-d.

## NUTRITIONAL ASPECTS OF THE APPLE

Just as we, the Jewish people, are not on the spiritual level of our ancestors, so the apple, to which we are likened, is not on a nutritional par with apples of the past. All fruits have decreased in nutritional value since Adam and Eve first ate them. [*Chesed l'Avraham* 19] The decline continued, as the Talmud explains, and after the destruction of the Temple the fruits declined even more rapidly. [Talmud, *Sotah* 48a] The apple is now practically devoid of major nutrients, as the chart below indicates.

| APPLE – raw, unpeeled[1] – 4.6 ounces (138 g.) | | | |
|---|---|---|---|
| Nutrient | Amount | U.S. RDA (Amount required each day.) | |
| | | Men (25-50 years) | Women (25-50 years) |
| calcium | 10 mg. | 800 mg. | 800 mg. |
| calories | 81 | 2900 | 2200 |
| carbohydrate | 21 g. | 363 g. | 275 g. |
| copper | 0.05 mg. | 2.3 mg. | 2.3 mg |
| fat | 0.5 g. | 96.7 g. | 73.3 g. |
| fiber | 2.8 g. | (no RDA) | (no RDA) |
| folacin | 4 mcg. | 200 mcg. | 180 mcg. |
| iron | 0.25 mg. | 10 mg. | 15 mg. |
| magnesium | 6 mg. | 350 mg. | 280 mg. |
| manganese | 0.06 mg. | 3.5 mg. | 3.5 mg. |
| niacin | 0.11 mg. | 19 mg. | 15 mg. |
| phosphorus | 10 mg. | 800 mg. | 800 mg. |
| potassium | 159 mg. | 2000 mg. | 2000 mg. |
| protein | 0.3 g. | 63 g. | 50 g. |
| riboflavin | 0.02 mg. | 1.7 mg. | 1.3 mg. |
| thiamin | 0.02 mg. | 1.5 mg. | 1.1 mg. |
| vitamin A | 74 IU | 3333 IU | 2667 IU |
| vitamin $B_6$ | 0.07 mg. | 2 mg. | 1.6 mg. |
| vitamin $B_{12}$ | 0 | 2 mcg. | 2 mcg. |
| vitamin C | 8 mg. | 60 mg. | 60 mg. |
| zinc | 0.05 mg. | 15 mg. | 12 mg. |

Source: Jean A.T. Pennington, *Bowes and Church Food Values of Portions Commonly Used.* Harper & Row, Publisher. 18th edition, 2004.

Despite its dismal nutritional appearance, the apple does contain various healing agents, which are not apparent when one uses standard procedures of assessing nutritional composition. These healing agents relate to both of today's greatest health problems: heart disease and cancer. The apple contains agents that can lower blood cholesterol levels, a major risk factor in heart disease, as well as cancer-preventing agents.

Antioxidants (phytochemicals present in apples in very small amounts) are powerful cancer and heart disease preventers. Flavonoids are polyphenolic antioxidants that occur naturally in vegetables and fruits, and apples are a major source of flavonoids. Flavonoids help to lower blood cholesterol levels and prevent blood clotting, thus reducing the likelihood of a fatal heart attack. Flavonoid intake has been shown to have an inverse correlation with mortality from coronary heart disease.[2] Apples also contain nutritional fiber, which has a protective influence on our health. Nutritionists generally speak of two types of fiber, soluble and insoluble. Soluble fibers are non-nutrient components that are soluble in water; insoluble fibers are not water-soluble. The apple, fortunately, contains both types of fiber, with all of their disease-preventing benefits.

The soluble fibers have the potential to lower serum lipid levels (fats, i.e., cholesterol, triglycerides). Pectin, a major soluble fiber, is present in significant amounts in apples. Apples are the most common food source for cholesterol-lowering pectin. The apple peel, which mainly consists of insoluble or undigested fiber, has long been noted for its anti-constipation and anti-cancer potential.

Every apple, then, has the potential to contribute to our health!

**HEAL US, O L-RD**

Abraham Ibn Ezra interprets the first two words of *Song of Songs* 2:5 as meaning: "Invigorate me with apples." Rashi comments on this that our Sages advised giving apples to the sick to heal them. Today the apple is still a symbol of good health, as reflected in the popular folk saying, "An apple a day keeps the doctor away."

The *Zohar* speaks of the apple's healing quality: "Just as the apple heals all, so the Holy One, blessed be He, heals all." [*Zohar*, Acharei Mos]

The *Zohar* continues: "Just as the apple has various colors (white, red, green), so the Holy One, blessed be He, has various supernal colors (white, red, and green, corresponding to the attributes of chesed [kindness], gevurah [severity], and Tiferes [beauty])." [*Zohar*, Acharei Mos; *Ziv ha-Zohar*, Va'eschanan]

The symbol of the green apple reveals some of the hidden meaning behind the *Zohar's* teaching. Tiferes, the kabbalistic attribute of mercy and beauty, is associated with the color green, the color of healing.

The patriarch Jacob (Ya'akov), has a special connection to health, as the Talmud relates: "Our father Yaakov did not die." [*Ta'anis* 5b] Yaakov is the patriarch associated with the attribute of Tiferes (or tiferet) or balance, as he represents the harmony between the aspects of kindness and severity. Likewise, Yaakov is associated with apples, as Yitzchak (Isaac) sensed a fragrance of apples, which entered with Yaakov when he came for his father's blessing, as explained previously.

The Ben Ish Chai writes that the apple tree is the only fruit tree that has its spiritual source in the attribute of tiferet. This is yet another indication of the apple's special connection to healing. [*Halachos*, Nitzavim]

Tiferes and healing are attributes which, for the Jew, may operate on a supernatural level. Our request for health is the eighth blessing in the weekday Shmona Esrey prayer:

> "Heal us, O L-rd, and we shall be healed; help us and we
> shall be saved; for You are our praise. Grant complete
> cure and healing to all our wounds; for You, Almighty
> King, are a faithful and merciful healer. Blessed are You,
> L-rd, Who heals the sick of His people Israel."

As G-d created the universe in seven days, the number eight connotes "above nature," beyond the usual natural order. Brit mila (circumcision) is generally performed on the eighth day after the birth of a Jewish male child. The brit itself is a sign that the Jew is connected to G-d on a supra-natural level. Raphael, the angel of Tiferes, came disguised as a guest to heal Abraham on the third day after his circumcision. [Rashi, *Genesis* 18:2]

The ineffable four-letter Name of G-d, which we respectfully refer to as yud-kay-vav-kay, symbolizes G-d's transcendence and control of nature. This Name is associated with the attribute of Tiferes. [*Be'er Mayim Chayim*, V'Eschanan] The tetragrammaton (Hebrew name for G-d) is the central Name of G-d, and all other Divine Names are secondary to it. [*Pri Tzaddik*, Volume 5, 134] By the strength of this Name, the nature of the universe can be broken. [*Be'er Mayim Chayim*, V'Eschanan]

The *Zohar* tells us that everything in Creation is inscribed with this special Name of G-d. It is His trademark on everything, showing Who created it. [*Zohar, Raya Mehemna*, V'Eschanan] It is like the hidden signature of an artist on his paintings.

With this in mind, if we cut an apple open along its horizontal axis, we can find markings that suggest G-d's inscription of His holy Name on the apple itself. In the accompanying diagram we see four types of markings on the apple that correspond to the four letters of the tetragrammaton:

I heard this interpretation of the apple from Rabbi Abraham Brandwein, the Rebbe of Stretin, of the Old City of Jerusalem. On Sabbath eves, some kabbalistic rabbis give apples to their students.

1.   The letter *yud* (numeric value = 10) is indicated by the ten dots in the pulp surrounding the seeds.

2.   The letter *kay* (substituting for the letter *hey* of the numeric equivalent 5) is indicated by the five seed spaces in the core of the apple.

3.   The shape of the letter *vav* is drawn by the stem.

4.   The second *kay* (substituting for the letter *hey* of the numeric equivalent 5) is indicated by the five seeds.

If we eat an apple with the proper intention, and if we serve G-d with the strength that we gain from eating this apple, we thereby join ourselves to G-d in holiness.

Upon leaving Egypt, the Jewish people were informed that G-d and His Torah are their source of healing:

> If you obey G-d your L-rd and do what is right in His
> eyes, carefully heeding all His commandments and
> keeping all His decrees, then I will not strike you with any
> of the sicknesses that I brought on Egypt. I am G-d Who
> heals you. [*Exodus* 15:26]

Spiritual health is the source of our physical health. Torah is the remedy. Spiritual perfection – full Torah observance – is the gateway to physical health. May we connect ourselves, like apples, to the tree of G-d and unite with His attribute of Tiferes. When we fully cleave to G-d and Torah, the Tree of Life, we shall be healed.

> Blessed are You, L-rd our G-d, King of the Universe,
> Creator of numerous living beings and their needs, for all
> the things You have created with which to sustain the soul
> of every living being. Blessed is He Who is the life of the
> worlds. [Borei Nefashos]

# *Reference*

1.  Pennington, JAT. *Bowes and Church Food Values of Portions Commonly Used,* 18th edition. New York: Harper & Row Publisher; 2004.

2.  Hertog M, Feskens EJM, Kromhout D, et al. Dietary antioxidant flavonoids and risk of coronary heart disease: the Zutphen Elderly Study. *The Lancet.* 1993; vol. 342: Issue 8878: pp. 1007-1011.

# Chapter 8

## Sabbath Nourishment and King David's Meal

"Like the World-to-Come, Sabbath, the day of rest..."
[Sabbath Zemiros]

"You need to know that everything one eats on the Sabbath, not only is it not harmful... it is healing!" These holy words, which the late Rebbe of Lelov (Rabbi Moshe Mordechai Biderman, of blessed memory) spoke to me during his Sabbath evening meal in Tiberius, Israel, made a lasting impression in my mind. The Rebbe was often heard commenting, "a taste of the Garden of Eden" after sampling his Sabbath food. After each Friday night meal, the Hassidim danced with the Rebbe to the song (Mei-ain Olam Ha-ba, "Like the World-to-Come, Sabbath the day of rest ..."). From practically every moment of the Rebbe's tish (community meal hosted by the Rebbe), one could sense the spirituality invested in the Sabbath nourishment, as the Rebbe tasted the foods and then distributed them to his disciples. From these experiences, I became inspired to explore the spirituality of eating, and in particular, to examine the spirituality invested in the Sabbath foods.

The story goes that a Roman ruler in the times of the Talmud once asked Rebbe Yehoshua, the son of Chanania, the following question: "Why do the Sabbath foods have such a fragrant aroma?" The Tanna answered that we have a special seasoning called "The Sabbath" which we add to these foods, and this spice causes the special fragrance. The Roman ruler demanded, "Give me also some of this Sabbath spice!" Rebbe Yehoshua answered that only he who keeps the Sabbath as a holy day is helped by this special spice. [Talmud, *Shabbos* 119]

We see from these stories that Sabbath nourishment has a special character not found in our usual eating. It is written in the prayer book of the holy Ari, the great Safed Kabbalist, that when one eats on the Sabbath, even more than one needs, the nourishment does not go to the "other side" (the side opposite to holiness) as it does during the week. Rather, it is totally absorbed in holiness. [*Chamisha Mamaros, Toras Shabbos* 308] Therefore, that which one eats in honor of the Sabbath is totally spiritual and holy. [*Siduro shel Shabbos* 5:3;7; *Minchas Shabbos* 72:31] On the Sabbath, the Divine Presence (Shachina) and all of the spiritual worlds benefit and are blessed from the eating itself, as is taught in the holy *Zohar*. [Vayakel 218a]

In the writings of the holy Ari, we learn that through the Sabbath and holiday eating, one can, theoretically, rise to a higher spiritual level than through prayer! [*Toras Avos l'Shabbos*] Just before the Sabbath, the good of klipas noga (mystical category that includes physical food) is separated from the evil in the supernal worlds, and all the foods as we enter the Sabbath consist of only good, and therefore do not need rectification. Through the pleasure of the Sabbath eating, supernal pleasure is drawn down, so to speak, and the food is elevated and included in the supernal pleasure of the Infinite light. [*Tamei ha-Mitzvos l'Zemach Zedek*, mitzvas lo tivaru esh]

We have learned that the Sabbath foods contain only good elements and therefore need no rectification. This places the Sabbath food on the level of the fruits of the Garden of Eden, the matzoh which the Jews ate as they left Egypt, the manna which they ate for forty years as they wandered in the desert, and the healing fruits which we shall eat, G-d willing, in the World-to-Come!

In the Talmud, Reish Lokish explains that an "additional soul" is given to a Jew who honors the Sabbath. [Talmud, *Taanis* 23b] This "additional soul" is nourished by the spirituality contained in the Sabbath foods.

Rabbi Shimon the son of Pazi said, all who eat the three Sabbath meals will be saved from three disasters, from the throes of the Messiah, from the judgment of the inferno, and from the war of Gog and Magog. [Talmud, *Shabbos* 118]

## THE SABBATH TABLE

The Sabbath table is set to represent the configuration of the inner chamber, the heichal, of the ancient Temple in Jerusalem. As in the Temple, the table, according to kabbalistic tradition is directed from north to south, with the breads on the northern end, as were the showbreads on the golden table, and the Sabbath candles on the southern end, as was the Temple olive oil lamp. On the Sabbath table, as on the altar of the Temple, is a knife to cut the challah bread, representing the knife used to slaughter the sacrifices, and salt, which was always offered with each sacrifice. The table is covered by a cloth representing the covering of dew which was below the manna. The two challah breads represent the double portion of manna which the Jews received before the Sabbath, in place of the single daily portion. These breads are also covered by a challah cloth or dekel to represent the upper layer of dew which surrounded the manna.

## FRIDAY NIGHT MEAL

The Friday night meal, according to kabbalistic tradition of the holy Ari, represents the meal of the "field of the holy apples." The Kaf ha-Chaim brings in his Code of Law that "one should very much try to have apples on his Sabbath table, especially during the Friday night meal. This hints at the aspect of malchut, which is called the field of the holy apples, as is known." [Kaf ha-Chaim 250: 7-15]

According to Jewish tradition, we begin the Friday night meal with a sanctification of the Sabbath and the blessing of Kiddush on a cup of wine. The seventy words of the Kiddush are the numerical equivalent of the Hebrew word for wine. All the worlds are crowned with seventy crowns by the precious praises of the seventy words of the Kiddush prayer, as is explained in the Friday night song of the holy Ari. The kabbalists teach us that wine hints at the spiritual world of binah, and that there is hidden the secret of the "preserved wine," the wine that the righteous will drink in the World-to-Come.

We recite the blessing, "who creates the fruit of the vine," specifically gefen (the vine) and not "wine" (yain). In the text Tamei ha-minhagim, it is explained that this unusual wording hints to us that the reciting of Kiddush causes a rectification of the original sin of Adam when he ate from the Tree of Knowledge.

And as the kabbalists teach us through reciting the words of the Kiddush, the Divine Presence (Shachina) descends spiritually below and abides, so to speak, above his table. [*Tamei ha-Minhagim*, Inyanei Shabbos 115]

### Bread

After the traditional hand washing and blessing, another blessing is then recited over the two challah breads. The challah is cut with a knife and each slice is dipped in salt and then eaten, as was traditional with each Temple sacrifice. Our table, then, represents the altar, and the food, our sacrifice. According to kabbalistic tradition, the blessing is recited over twelve breads, symbolic of the twelve showbreads, as in the ancient Temple. [*Vayikra* 24: 5-9]

It is customary in the Jewish home to bake breads in honor of the Sabbath, and for the women to separate a portion of the dough as challah, which during the times of Temple was given to the Priests (now it is burned). Proverbially, when G-d created the world, He separated a small piece of earth, which He formed into Adam, the first man, symbolically representing the challah of the world. When Eve (Chava), the first woman, fed Adam the forbidden fruit from the Tree of Knowledge just before the first Sabbath, she symbolically blemished the challah of the world. When women now divide challah from the dough, they help rectify this original wrongdoing. [*Tamei ha-Minhagim*, Shabbos 115, Shulchan Aruch, *Orach Chaim* 242, 1, *Mishna Brurah* 6] When women light the Sabbath candles just before the Sabbath begins, this returns some of the light that was extinguished at that time.

**Beginning of the Meal**

It is traditional to begin the Friday night meal with fish, and to eat fish at each of the three Sabbath meals. [*Magen Avraham* 242,3]  The Hebrew word for fish is dag (dalet, gimmel), and it has a numerical value (gematria) of seven – where aleph is 1, beis is 2, gimmel is 3, dalet is 4, etc. – so dalet plus gimmel is 4 plus 3 or 7. Seven represents the Sabbath, the seventh day of the week!

*Ground Foods*

The Ashkenazic custom is to include ground fish (gefilte) often together with ground horseradish (krein), and many other ground foods, as well, during the various Sabbath meals.  Farfel, boiled clumps of flour, is often served on Friday night. These ground foods are a further hint at the vitalizing manna, which came ground for the righteous, and was the source of all foods. [*Arvei Nachal*, Bahalosecha]

Jewish tradition teaches that in the supernal world of shachakim, spiritual millstones will grind the manna for the righteous in the World-to-Come. [*Tamei ha-Minhagim* 373; Talmud, *Chagiga* 12b]

As King David recites in Psalms:

> And shachakim went forth from above, and the doors of Heaven opened, and the manna rained upon them for their food ... [*Psalms* 78:23]

Examples of other ground foods, often traditionally eaten during the Sabbath, include chopped eggs with onion, potato and noodle pudding (kugel), clumped wheat flour (farfel), dough balls (kneidelach), and chopped liver.

## Main Meal

*Fish*

Returning now to fish, we learn that fish, due to their extreme degree of righteousness, did not perish in the worldwide flood at the time of Noah (Noach). As well, according to kabbalistic tradition, most of the righteous souls that must return to the world in a further reincarnation (gilgul), come back as fish. Through proper eating of these holy fish on the Sabbath, their souls can have a rectification. [*Kitzur Shloh* Hanhagas Shabbos 161]

A further reason is that fish have no eyelids, and their eyes are therefore always open. This hints at the Holy One, blessed be He, whose "eyes," so to speak, are always open to watch over us with great mercy. [*Tamei ha-Minhagim* in the name of *Minchas Yaakov*]

Traditionally, after the fish portion, a l'chaim (translated as "to life") is drunk from an alcoholic beverage, and a small piece of challah bread is eaten, before the meat portion.

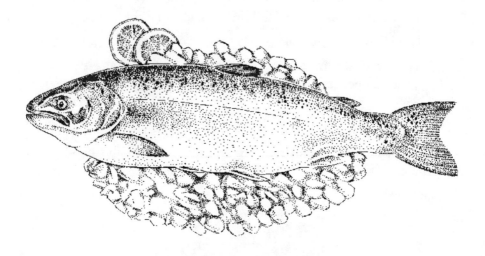

*Chicken Soup*

At this point, chicken soup is customarily served. As explained previously, foods eaten on the Sabbath generally show a numerical value of seven, as calculated via the gematria system (aleph=1, beis=2, etc.) or some alternative calculation (like mispar katan, reducing the tens or hundreds), using the Hebrew word for the food. Challah is ches 8, lamed 30, hei 5 = 43, which breaks up to 4 plus 3 = 7. Yain, Hebrew for wine, is yud 10, yud 10, nun 50 = 70 (mispar katan 7, eliminating the zero). The Kiddush itself has 70 words, mispar katan 7. Likewise, marak, Hebrew for soup, is mem 40, reish 200, kuf 100=4 plus 2 plus 1 in mispar katan = 7. Basar, the Hebrew word for meat is beis 2, sin 300, reish 200 = 2 plus 3 plus 2 = 7 in mispar katan!

The soup often includes a ground food, as well, such as matzah balls (kneidelach), noodles (made from flour from ground wheat), or soup nuts (mandelach or shekedai marak).

After the soup, it is traditional to eat meat or chicken. The taste of onion and garlic were not included in the manna, as we discussed, since they bothered nursing infants. It is customary to add these to our Sabbath foods during their preparation to complete the taste of our Sabbath food.

## Daytime Sabbath Meals

During the daytime meal, after the chopped eggs and onion, a hot course is generally served, consisting of chulent (the Ashkenazic custom) or chamin (the Sephardic custom), often accompanied by kugel (Yiddish) or pashtedah (Hebrew), potato or noodle pudding. The covered hot food, consisting of meat or chicken, and potato, rice or buckwheat, plus beans or barley, is set on a covered fire or electric hotplate before the onset of the Sabbath. It is taken off the heat source just before it is served, during the daytime meal. Besides its superior taste (oneg of Shabbos - Sabbath delight) as a hot food, it emphasizes our belief in the Oral Law (Mishneh), which permits us to eat hot food on the Sabbath, if it was held in this prescribed manner (but not initially cooked on the Sabbath).

At the conclusion of the meals, the blessings are recited as is customary in a meal including bread, as discussed in the chapter on food blessings.

In the Sabbath foods, we witness the combination of the signs of Creation and hints of the World-to-Come. The Sabbath foods are a taste of this future time – each week.

## KING DAVID'S MEAL: MELAVA MALKA

> A psalm, a poem for the Sabbath day. It is a good thing to give thanks to the L-rd, and to sing praise to thy name, O most High ... [*Psalms* 92]

An additional meal is traditionally eaten after the close of the Sabbath and the havdalah ceremony. This is known as "King David's meal" or "Melava Malka," translated as "accompanying the Queen." This most important meal is eaten with the intention of escorting the Sabbath Queen (Divine Presence, Shachina) who departs from us at this time at the close of the Sabbath. This meal is a symbol of the Final Redemption and of eternal life, which will soon be explained.

Tradition teaches us that our redeemer or Messiah (Moshiach) will be a descendant of King David, and his coming will be heralded by the Prophet Elijah. It is said that this will not occur on the Sabbath, so the earliest time each week is after the close of the Sabbath. It's no coincidence, then, that these two personalities are associated with this important meal! To further explain, King David, after he inquired, was told by G-d that his life would end on the Sabbath, but exactly which Sabbath was hidden from him. When each Sabbath passed, and he saw that he was still alive, he celebrated with a feast. In his merit and memory, and in gratitude for the beautiful psalms which he has left us, we celebrate, as well, each week by eating the Melave Malka meal.

The story goes that there was an ancient city called Luz, whose inhabitants never died within the city limits. This was in the same location, apparently no coincidence, where our Patriarch Jacob (Ya'akov) lied down to rest and dreamed of a ladder reaching to heaven, with angels ascending and descending on it. He awoke and exclaimed,

> This is no other than the house of G-d, and this is the gate
> of heaven... and he called the name of that place Bet-el
> (House of G-d); but the name of that city was called Luz
> at first. [*Genesis* 27:10]

The ancient city itself was established by a man who was freed by the Jews during a war in the Holy Land, described as follows:

> ... and the man went into the land of the Hittim, and
> built a city, and called its name Luz: which is the name to
> this day. [*Judges* 1: 22]

The city had a tradition that it would never be destroyed. It was never conquered by Sancheirev, and was not destroyed by Nevuchadnetzar, King of Babylon, even though both invaded it. The people of Luz were known to always tell the truth. The Angel of Death had no permission to pass through it. When the elderly felt it was time, they were carried outside of the city's wall, and they passed away outside of the city. Luz is where they made the blue dye (techeles) for the fringes of the Jewish prayer shawl. [Midrash, *Bereshis Rabba* 69: 8]

Luz is also the name of a special bone in the body, where the skull and the spine meet. It is a wondrous secret that the rabbis named this bone Luz. Tradition has it that this bone does not decay in the grave, and it is from this bone that man will be brought back to life in the times of the revival of the dead. This bone which lives on forever was called Luz, like the city Luz, where no man ever died. [Midrash, *Tanna d'vei Eliyahu Zuta* 16, *Zikkukin* 156]

What is especially important to us here is that the sages tell us that this bone receives its nourishment through the meal of Melava Malka! [*Tur, Beit Yosef* 300] It is therefore, recommended to eat the Melava Malka meal as soon as possible after the havdalah ceremony, in order to eat it when not hungry, having just recently concluded the third Sabbath meal. This sanctified eating, "for the sake of Heaven," not due to hunger, but intended to escort the Sabbath Queen with an honorable meal, accompanied by songs and stories of Elijah the Prophet, provides weekly nourishment to the Luz bone.

We have previously quoted Elijah the Prophet as blaming each person's death on improper eating (that is, eating not "for the sake of Heaven"). Due to its great importance to the matter at hand, it is herein repeated:

> I call heaven and earth to bear witness that all the children
> of man are gathered to death and all creatures descend to
> sorrow only because of eating and drinking. [Midrash, *Tanna
> d'vei Eliyahu Zuta* 3]

With this in mind, we can understand that when Adam sinned in the Garden of Eden and ate from the Tree of Knowledge, his entire body received benefit from that forbidden food, except, as our sages tell us, for the Luz bone. Adam was ultimately punished for this improper eating with death, which was passed on to all generations. Our sages tell us that when one dies his body decays and turns back to dust, from which it was formed. The Luz bone, contrary to this according to Jewish tradition, does not decay, but remains intact. [*Zohar*, Vaeira] It is from this bone that, at the end of days, will come the Revival of the Dead. [*Eliyahu Rabba* in *Tamei ha-Minhagim*, Shabbos]

The Talmud tells us that eating hot food after the Sabbath is healing. [Talmud, *Shabbos* 119] One opinion is that it heals us from sadness, since we feel at a loss when the Sabbath departs.

We see, then, that the Melava Malka meal is a most spiritual and important meal. Together with the Luz bone which it nourishes, they are symbols of the Final Redemption and of eternal life.

# Chapter 9

# Other Spiritual Teachings

## MANNA

> ...He commanded the clouds from above, and opened the doors of heaven, and rained down manna upon them of the corn of heaven. [*Psalms* 78: 24]

### Descent of the Manna

On the fifteenth day of the Hebrew month of Iyar, in the year 2448 B.C.E. after Creation, a breath-taking sight occurred in the skies of the Sinai desert. Less than one month earlier the Jewish people had fled from Egypt and a life of slavery through G-d's Divine intervention, with the miraculous splitting of the Red Sea.

Then, as a sign of G-d's continued faithfulness, He blessed them with manna, the finest food that man has ever known, referred to as the "food of angels." G-d had given them an example of an ideal food and of the ideal way to eat through His provision of the manna in the Sinai desert, as their preparation for the future receiving of the Torah on Mount Sinai.

During the night, dew had descended and collected on the cold, desert sand. Upon this layer of dew the manna fell and was then covered by another layer of dew. The manna, then, rested in a container of dew during the night. [Rashi, *Exodus* 16:14] The Jews collected their day's rations of the manna. What remained was warmed thoroughly by the sun within four hours, forming flowing rivers of liquid manna. [Talmud, *Brochos* 27] The rams and the deer drank thirstily from these streams. When the nations of the world later took these animals for food, they experienced the taste of manna in the animal's flesh.

Upon leaving Egypt, the Jews ate matzoh, the unleavened bread which also had the taste of manna. [Talmud, *Kedushin* 38a] Now, in the wilderness they ate manna in preparation for receiving the Torah at Mount Sinai. This "bread from heaven" was from a high supernal source, as G-d said to Moses: "Behold, I will rain bread from heaven for you." [*Beshalach* 16:4]

Rabbi Shimon bar Yochai explains in his holy kabbalistic book, the *Zohar*, that the manna descended from the most hidden of the hidden primordial worlds of supernal dew. [Bahalosicha 13] This holy, supernal dew dripped down to the worlds below. As it descended its light illuminated all the worlds. It nourished the field of the holy apples, dwelling place of the souls, and the supernal angels. As it continued its descent into the air of the world, it was solidified, frozen, in a sense, and its brilliance was altered. The manna was like coriander seed and its appearance was like that of bidolach (crystal stone) ... and no more. Manna was originally created by G-d as one of the ten things created just before the first Sabbath during the creation of the world. [Mishna, *Avos* 5:8]

The manna began its descent during the Hebrew month of Iyar. This month is thereby considered a propitious time for medicine and healing, as no illness ever resulted from eating the manna, contrary to other foods. Manna was a perfect food for human consumption and blessed the Jews with radiant health. [*Bnei Yissachar*, Maamrei Chodesh Iyar, 3]

The children of Israel subsequently ate manna for forty years. Upon the passing of Moses on the seventh day of the Hebrew month of Adar, the manna ceased to fall. [Rashi, *Exodus* 17:35] We received the manna due to the great merit of Moses our Teacher, and when he passed from the world, the manna ceased. [Talmud, *Taanis* 9a]

**Description of the Manna**

> And when the layer of dew was gone up, behold, upon the
> face of the wilderness there lay a fine flaky substance, as fine
> as the hoar frost on the ground. [*Exodus* 7: 14]

The commentator Rashi elaborates on the appearance of the manna,
explaining that it was thin, round, and pearl-white like bidolach, crystal stone. [Rashi, *Exodus* 17:14, 31] [Talmud, *Yoma 75*] [Rashi, *Numbers*
11:7]

It had a doughy consistency, like dough that has been fried in honey.
[Rashi, *Exodus* 17:31] It looked like white seeds named "coriander," (an
herb, *coriander sativum*, is an aromatic black seed used for seasoning).
[Rashi, *Exodus* 17:31] [Ibn Ezra, *Sekhel Tov*]

Rabbi Ashi comments in the Talmud that the manna was white, as
it had a whitening or cleansing effect on the sins of Israel. Rashi explains
that since the Jews worried that perhaps the manna would cease to fall the
following day, they would therefore turn their hearts in prayer to G-d for
their continued sustenance. [Talmud, *Yoma* 75] It would literally "melt in
your mouth" as soon as it was eaten.

**Taste**

> ...and the taste of it was like dough made with honey.
> [*Exodus,* Beshalach 16:31]

Manna was given to teach us satisfaction with our portion. If there
had been a difference in appearance or fragrance between the various
portions, jealousy may have developed among the recipients. It's simple,
white appearance prevented this problem. Taste, on the other hand, is personal. Each person who ate the manna experienced an individual taste,
one known only to himself. [*Menachem Tzion*, 51] Rashi explains that the
manna was like a dough kneaded in oil mixed with honey. [Rashi, *Numbers*
11:8] The Talmud explains that the "taste of all foods was tasted in the
manna."[Talmud, *Yoma* 75] It drew the hearts of men to eat it, as its wondrous taste contained all possible tastes. [Talmud, *Yoma 75, Maharsha*] Its

taste is referred to as sixty times sweeter than honey. [*Chupas Eliyahu Raba* 5, 2] In other words, honey is one-sixtieth as sweet as manna, which helps us conceptualize its phenomenal taste, somewhat. Manna is referred to as "bread," "oil," and "honey." [*Menachem Tzion* 50] Rabbi Yosi, the son of Rabbi Chanina, explains that it was bread to the youth, oil to the elderly, and honey for the small children. [Talmud, *Yoma* 75b]

The manna descended for each person personalized to fit each temperament, according to age, and according to the health of one's body, in order not to cause any harm. [*Midrash Raba*, Bishalach] Tastes that were harmful to pregnant or nursing women, for example, such as onions and garlic, were not experienced. [Talmud, *Yoma,* 75a, Rashi]  Five tastes were not sensed in the manna, which were foods that were unhealthy in those times and which made Torah learning difficult. [*Numbers* 11:5, Rashi] [*Pesikta Zutra*, Beha' alosicha] [*Ein Yaakov*, Yoma 75, citing the Rambam, *Hilchos Deos,* 4] An additional opinion describes that all tastes and food textures were experienced when the manna was eaten, but with these five foods, only tastes were experienced but textures were not. [Talmud, *Yoma* 75a]

Each person could experience the taste he desired when eating the manna by simply thinking about it! Manna was the source of all foods. It therefore contained all possible tastes. Moses explained to the Jewish people that manna would be the food of the righteous in the World-to-Come. [Talmud, *Yoma* 75, *Maharsha*] In the supernal world of shachakim, millstones will grind the manna for the righteous in the World-to-Come.

Manna, then, was the source of all foods. [*Arvei Nachal*, Beha' alosicha] It was a spiritual food from the World of Thought. Through the manna, all foods were sustained in their existence, receiving their vital life-force through the essence of the manna. The Arve Nachal explains that each physical entity has its spiritual root. The ultimate root of all physicality in the World of Thought is totally good. The Holy One, blessed be He, wanted to purify the Jewish people.  He therefore fed them with a food that was totally good and spiritual, descending from the World of Thought, which is only good. As thought can be altered at will, the taste of the manna could therefore be altered at will, according to the desires of the one who was eating it. [*Arvei Nachal*, Beha' alosicha]

**Collecting the Manna**

> And they gathered it every morning, every man according
> to his eating; and when the sun grew hot, it melted.
> [*Exodus* 16:21]

The manna was collected each weekday morning and was put aside until the evening, when it was immediately eaten. [Midrash, *Tanna deVei Eliyahu Raba* 18] The Talmud elaborates that together with the manna fell perfumes, which the women ground and anointed themselves to smell pleasant for their husbands, plus spices for tasty cooking, and precious stones and pearls. [*Yoma* 75a] [Rashi, *Yoma* 75a]

The righteous, who trusted completely in G-d, found the manna just outside their door, ready-to-eat, like bread. The average man went out daily to collect cakes of manna which still required baking. Evil people were also fed, but they travelled far to collect their manna ration, and they had to first grind it in a mill before baking. [Talmud, *Yoma* 75] Legal judgments made by Moses between disputing parties were often confirmed by noting where the manna portion appeared on the following morning. [Talmud, *Yoma* 75a]

> And it came to pass, that on the sixth day they gathered a
> double portion, two omer for one man.  [*Exodus* 16:22]

The manna fell from the heavens to the earth during the six weekdays, comparable to the weekday influx of all physicality from its spiritual heavenly source. [*Kedushas Levi*, Beshalach] The day prior to the Sabbath, G-d sent a double portion to provide the Jews with food for the Sabbath without requiring additional collection. This Sabbath manna, contrary to the usual weekday portion, miraculously, did not spoil when left overnight!

## Eating the Manna

> This is the thing which the L-rd has commanded, Gather of
> it every man according to his eating, an omer for every man,
> according to the number of your persons shall you take it, every
> man for them who are in his tent. [*Exodus* 16:16]

Each Jew ate a daily portion of one omer (approximately three quarts),
no more and no less. [*Exodus* 16:35] An omer was one-tenth of an eipha.
(Note: Rashi explains in *Exodus* 16:36 that an eipha is three sahin. A sah
is six kavin, a kav is four lugin, and a lug is six beitzim or six eggs. It comes
out the one-tenth of an eipha is forty-three and one-fifth eggs, which is
the amount for challah tithe and for the mincha sacrificial offering, which
was brought to the altar at the ancient Temple in Jerusalem.) Larger families received a relatively larger portion than smaller families. No jealousy
arose, as everyone received an equivalent amount, each person according to
his nutritional needs, "Each man according to his eating." [Rashi, *Exodus*
16:16] Nevertheless, there were those who took more than their prescribed
portion, and some that took less. Miraculously, when they returned home
and measured their portions, all measured exactly alike, the prescribed
omer portion! [Rashi, *Exodus* 16:17]

The manna was a heavenly food, the food of the ministering angels.
[Midrash, *Tanna deVei Eliyahu Raba* 14] It is also the food of the souls of
the righteous in Heaven. [Talmud, *Chagiga* 12] The eating of this holy food
brought the Jewish people to a spiritual level where they were able to accept
the Torah. [Mechiltah, *Beshalach* 17] The Rebbe Menachem Mendel of
Riminov explains that the Hebrew word for manna, mn, is an abbreviation
for mayin nukvin (translated as feminine waters, a kabbalistic concept).
Eating manna caused one to experience a personal arousal towards spirituality, just as the mystical feminine waters awakens the masculine waters
above. [*Menachem Tzion* 53] The manna was, then, a special food for the
soul.

Before beginning to eat the manna, the Jews recited the following blessing:

"Blessed are You, L-rd our G-d, King of the Universe, who brings forth bread from the heavens" (instead of "bread from the earth").

Moses was inspired with the special *hazan* blessing when the manna first began to fall. [Talmud, *Berochos* 48] This blessing was thereafter recited after the Jews ate their daily manna portion, and was later included as the first blessing after a meal where bread is eaten.

The manna was warm when it was eaten. [Talmud, *Yoma* 76a] Young men ate their manna as bread, the elderly like wafers made with honey, and the nursing children like milk from their mother's breast. The sick ate it like fine cereal mixed with honey. [Midrash, *Shemos Raba* 5]

Moses instructed the Jews not to leave the manna until morning. Two people, Dasan and Aviram, did leave over their portions which then turned wormy and rotten. [Rashi, *Exodus* 16:19-20]

And the children of Israel did eat the manna for forty years, until they came to an inhabited land. They did eat the manna, until they came to the borders of the land of Kena'an. [*Exodus* 16:35]

When Moses died the manna ceased to fall. Miraculously, the Jews were able to continue eating the manna that fell before Moses' passing on the seventh of Adar until the seventeenth of Nissan, over one month, until they went across the Jordan River into the Land of Israel. [Midrash, *Tanna deVai Eliyahu Raba* 18, *Zikukin* ]

## Digestion and Absorption of the Manna

Manna, the perfect food, was refined and soft. It melted upon eating or upon touch, and it was directly absorbed into the body. No residue remained for excretion from the intestines. [*Maharsha, Yoma* 75] Even foods obtained from non-Jewish merchants, when eaten together with the manna, were neutralized by the manna and also underwent total absorption, leaving no residue. [Talmud, *Yoma* 75b] Upon eating, the manna did not descend the esophagus to the stomach, as usual, in the process of digestion. The manna entered the windpipe (trachea) and from there proceeded to the heart and then on to nourish all the limbs of the body. [*Menachem Tzion* 47] It was completely absorbed and assimilated into the body.

Normally, one is nourished by physical foods which are in the mystical category of klipas noga. Though one digests the foods and retains their nourishing aspects, some trace still remains in one's body from the unclean klipas noga. The food thereby adds to one's physicality, lowering one's soul, and it causes one to draw after the physicality of the world. Even the most righteous, who eat with very holy spiritual intention, are left with a trace of physicality through their eating. Even the manna, which had an exalted spiritual origin, obtained some trace of physicality as it descended to the world and took on a physical form. For this reason, Moses fasted forty days before receiving the Torah. He did not eat even manna, as it also contained a trace of physicality. [*Likutei Torah,* Bamidbar 7, Rabbi Shneur Zalman of Liadi, the first Lubavitcher Rebbe]

Low residue nutritional formulas (chemically defined elemental diets) are the closest thing to the manna that man has produced. These formulas are extremely low in nutritional fiber, the indigestible component of most foods, and are therefore almost totally absorbed by the body. As one pharmaceutical company writes, "...requires virtually no digestion and as little as 100 centimeters of functional intestine for absorption. Because it is almost totally absorbed it yields negligible residue." It is produced as a fine, white powder which is administered to patients with limited ability to absorb food through their intestines. Astronauts are also given such food to prevent them from producing large amounts of waste material.

It is interesting to compare the nutritional composition of these formulas to the descriptions of the manna from scripture:

| Nutrient | Elemental Formula | Manna |
|---|---|---|
| Protein | pure amino acids | "coriander seed" |
| Fat | purified safflower oil | "fat of breast" |
| Carbohydrate | glucose oligosaccharides | 60 x sweeter than honey |

Nevertheless, in contrast to the manna, elemental formulas have an unappealing taste, are quite expensive, and are not completely absorbed by the body. Man has not succeeded, with all the available modern technology, in producing a food that truly compares to the manna. As explained in a prestigious nutrition textbook, as long as intestinal absorption is necessary in the digestion of food, no food can compare with the manna, which was 100% absorbed:

> The excretion of sloughed enterocytes, intestinal bacteria, and mucus results in some residue even if nothing is eaten. Therefore, no diet is residue-free. [*Clinical Nutrition and Dietetics,* Frances Zeman, Macmillan Pub. 1991, p. 267]

The manna, then, surpassed today's best nutritional formulas! Good taste, no cost, ready availability, complete absorbability, and kashrut (kosher), established it as the most perfect food ever known.

## Manna, a Symbol of Faith, Trust, and Sustenance

> And he humbled thee, and suffered thee to hunger, and fed thee with manna, which thou knewest not, neither did thy fathers know; that he might make thee known that man does not live by bread only, but by every word that proceeds out of the mouth of the L-rd does man live. [*Deuteronomy* 8:3]

As already mentioned, the Jews ate manna as a preparation for the receiving the Torah at Mount Sinai. [Mechilta, *Beshalach* 16:3] It had the spiritual effect of purifying their souls and bodies, resulting in their having absolute faith in G-d, in fulfilling his commandments, and in accepting the Torah unconditionally (naseh venishma in Hebrew). [*Menachem Tzion* 55] From this, we see that what we eat affects our spiritual awareness and sensitivity to spiritual matters, as discussed in the chapter on the kosher system of eating.

Manna had the effect of whitening the sins of Israel. Since the Jews worried each day that perhaps tomorrow the manna would cease to descend, they turned their hearts daily to G-d in prayer for their sustenance. [Talmud, *Yoma* 75, Rashi]

The students of Rabbi Shimon bar Yochai, author of the Zohar, once asked him, "Why did the manna not fall for Israel just once each year?" He answered with a parable. A king once had a son, to whom he gave sufficient funds to support him once each year. The king found that he thereafter only saw his son once a year. He decided to begin giving this son his income on a daily basis, and in this way he saw his son each day. Likewise, each Jewish man who himself had four or five children, would worry that perhaps tomorrow he would not receive the manna and his children would die from hunger. In this way, by sending the manna on a daily basis, each man would turn his heart to his Father-in-Heaven, and this way, G-d, would also see, so to speak, each of His children every day. [Talmud, *Yoma* 76a]

Elijah the Prophet, tells us that as a reward for the bread that our Patriarch Abraham fed his ministering angel guests, G-d gave us the manna in the wilderness for forty years. [*Tanna deVei Eliyahu*] He continues that Moses instructed Aaron, his brother, to fill a vessel (clay, Mechilta, Targum Yonasan, Rashi or glass, Rabbenu Chananel) with an omer of manna. He did this so that in later days the Prophet Jeremiah could beseech the Jews to trust in G-d by showing them this flask of manna, reminding them of how G-d fed them in the wilderness, insuring them that He would always provide their needs. Thereafter, the flask of manna was hidden together with the holy ark and other ritual items in a deep sepulcher under the Temple Mount. King Yoshiahu, worried that these holy objects would eventually be exiled to Babylonia, had them concealed for safe-keeping before the destruction of the First Temple. [Babylonian Talmud, *Yoma* 52b; Jerusalem

Talmud, *Shekalim* 16a] The Midrash explains that Elijah the Prophet will himself present this same vessel of manna to the Jewish people when he arrives to proclaim the Final Redemption. [Midrash, *Tanchuma,* Beshalach 21]

## EATING OF THE RIGHTEOUS

For the righteous, fasting and food restriction may be a path to holiness. But conversely, eating a lot of food with the right intention, which is perhaps more difficult, elevates the sparks or souls contained in these foods to a higher spiritual level. The person himself, who eats in a state of holiness receives an elevation of his spiritual status.

As we shall discuss, it is not just simply, "You are what you eat." What applies according to Jewish tradition is, "You are what and *how* you eat!" In the Jewish faith what is ultimately important is that one eats "for the sake of Heaven," for G-d, for a higher purpose, and not simply to satisfy one's natural desires.

One can approach this challenge either by food denial or by trying to eat for a higher, holy purpose. Not all, perhaps, can reach extremely elevated spiritual levels, and certainly not quickly without investing great effort, but each of us can succeed in improving his present spiritual level of eating and to work on it continuously to reach his maximum potential during his lifetime.

### Fasting of the Righteous

In the past, many pious Jews have served the Creator by intentionally denying themselves physical pleasure, subsisting on very little food. Many afflicted themselves by fasting to transcend, in a sense, the physical and to enter a more spiritual realm, as well as to atone for sin.

The Talmud tells of Rabbi Chanina the son of Dosa, saying that "the whole world continues to exist in his merit, and he subsists on just a *kav* of carob from one Sabbath to the next. [Talmud, *Taanis* 48]

Elijah the Prophet ate a simple meal of cake and water, and then travelled in the strength of that meal for forty days and forty nights to Horev, the mountain of G-d. [*Kings* 19:5-8]

The late Rebbe of Lelov, Rabbi Moshe Mordechai Biderman, may his memory be a blessing upon us, was especially careful to sanctify his eating. His custom was never to eat until he had immersed in a ritual pool (mikveh) to purify himself.

A famous story goes that the Baal Shem Tov, founder of the Hassidic movement, left home after the Sabbath to study and meditate in the forest with six loaves of bread, one for each day of the week. He returned just before the following Sabbath with the same six breads. He was questioned about this practice of fasting by his followers (hassidim), who understood that their master's way of serving G-d was through joy, and not through affliction and fasting. The holy Baal Shem Tov answered that they were correct, G-d should be served through joy and eating properly, and that he had not intended to fast. He had been so involved in his spiritual practices that he had simply forgotten to eat!

The Rebbe of Opt once ate very little, as too much food bothered his concentration during prayer and Torah study. He once spiritually perceived that the sparks of holiness or souls in various foods brought to him were complaining that due to the righteous man's habit of eating very little, they would not receive their spiritual rectification. From this time on, he began eating enormous amounts of food, and behold, the large quantities no longer affected his intense prayer and in-depth Torah study.

This idea of proper intention during eating can be taken on many levels – from simple good intentions up to the kabbalistic secrets of concentrations on various names of G-d before and during eating.

In summation, Jewish tradition converts eating, a physical activity necessary for our existence, to a spiritual service of the Creator. We recognize that there is a miraculous combination of the spiritual together with the physical in the practice of eating. The righteous discussed in this chapter should not be limited to those who fast or who eat with kabbalistic intentions – it includes all who dedicate their eating to a higher cause.

## A SPECIAL MEAL: EATING OF THE ANGELS

> Taking in guests is greater than receiving the face of the
> Divine Presence. [Talmud, *Shabbos* 127a]

Our eating can be taken one final step further. We can learn this from the eating of the angels who visited our first Patriarch Abraham, as he recovered from his circumcision.

After generations of chaos, where Adam and Eve sinned by eating from the Tree of Knowledge, where Cain killed Able, after the flood of Noah, and the tower of Babel – our Patriarch Abraham took on the massive task to begin rectifying the world through proper eating, by taking in guests, feeding them in holiness, and by teaching them to recognize and to thank the Creator.

G-d sent Abraham three very distinguished guests, ministering angels clothed in air-like garments which allowed them to take on human appearance. [*Zohar*, Vayera] Michoel, the angel of kindness, was sent to inform them that Abraham's wife, Sarah, would have a child in her old age. Gabriel, the angel of strength and severity, was sent to destroy the evil city of Sedom. Rifoel, the angel of beauty and healing, was sent to heal Abraham from his circumcision. Even though he was still weak and recovering from his recent circumcision three days prior, Abraham ran to greet his future guests. He saw they were angels of G-d, and he was immediately healed when he looked at Rifoel. [*Or Ha-Chaim*, Vayera]

He washed their feet and invited them to rest in the shade of his tree. The Zohar explains that Abraham was a reincarnation of Adam, the first man. Abraham rectified Adam's sin of improper eating by using his special tree, which represented the Tree of Life (Eshel Avraham in Hebrew), and by feeding his guests and having them praise G-d for the food which they ate. He first tested his guests to find out if they were truly willing to come to G-dliness by having them sit under his tree. For those that were fitting, the tree would lower its branches, enclosing them and providing them with shade. For those who were still connected to idol worship, the tree would lift up its branches completely.

Abraham did not tolerate that his guests would have to wait until he prepared the main course. He immediately brought before them butter and milk to eat. [*Beer Mayim Chaim*, Vayera] He was in the habit of preparing feasts for his guests comparable to those of King Solomon. [Talmud, *Baba Metzia* 86b] One of the three oxen which he had chosen to prepare tongues for the meal, suddenly bolted away, and Abraham himself chased it until it led him into the Cave of the Patriarchs in Hebron. [*Tanna deVei Eliyahu*, Yalkut 82]

As reward for Abraham's taking in these special guests, the Jews received many great benefits. As reward for the jug of water with which he washed the angels' feet, G-d gave us the well of water which accompanied us for forty years, as we travelled in the wilderness after our escape from Egyptian slavery. As reward for the shade of his tree in which he received the angels, G-d gave us seven clouds of glory which encompassed us as we travelled through the desert. As reward for the bread which Abraham fed the angels, G-d gave us the manna to eat in the desert, with its various tastes. As reward for the meat which Abraham fed the angels, G-d gave us quail meat twice in the desert. And as a reward for accompanying his guests, G-d accompanied us forty years as we travelled in the desert. [*Tanna deVei Eliyahu Rabba* 12]

Above, in Heaven, there is no eating or drinking. [*Midrash Rabba*, Vayera] For this reason, Moses fasted for forty days before receiving the Torah. He was nourished like an angel for forty days in Heaven, on a level even higher than the manna. [*Likutei Torah,* Bamidbar 7, Rabbi Shneur Zalman of Liadi]

We take our eating for granted, thinking of it simply as a physical act necessary for our survival. But the angels that visited Abraham wanted to eat his food, even though they were normally accustomed to nourishment in a much higher, spiritual way.

The commentator Rashi explains that the angels went through the motions of eating, deriving from this that one should not deviate from the accepted customs of his surroundings. [*Genesis* 18:8] One Midrashic opinion, states that they only appeared to eat. [*Yalkut Shimoni*, Vayera 18]

However, in contrast, the Midrash based on the teachings of Elijah the Prophet says that, "All that say that the ministering angels that visited Abraham our father did not eat, are saying nothing." Due to the righteousness of Abraham and the great efforts he exerted to take in his guests, G-d rewarded him by opening the angels' mouths and by causing them to eat. [*Tanna deVei Eliyahu Rabba* 12] Therefore, it says in scripture, "He stood over them under the tree and they ate." [*Genesis* 18:8] And the Midrash tells us that the angels had pleasure from this eating.

The holy *Zohar* explains, as well, that they "ate," or rather appeared to eat, as they certainly did not eat in our usual way. As they brought the food to their mouths, there shot forth a flaming fire from the angel which burned and completely consumed the food. This flame, however, was enclosed in a garment of air, and therefore was not noticed from the outside. They then consumed each flaming morsel of food, and their host Abraham had great pleasure from their eating. [*Zohar,* Vayera]

Rabbi Tzioni explains that the fire descended from G-d (through the angel) and licked up the food, as later occurred to the Prophet Elijah, when he offered water on an altar, and a fire from Heaven consumed it. [*Sefer Tzioni*, Vayera]

In this story is hidden the "secret of eating." After all, why did the angels want to eat physical food? In Heaven, the angels sing, "Holy, holy, holy is the L-rd of hosts; the whole earth is full of His glory." [*Isaiah* 6:3] They recognized that there is holiness in our physical world, which is filled with G-d's glory, and they wanted to share in this form of praise, as well. This story hints at the deep, mystical effects of eating, a taste of what is occurring in the realms above.

The Or Ha-Chayim tells us that Abraham knew that his guests were angels, but he still wanted to feed them, since there are great secrets hidden in the act of eating, as it is written, "The righteous man eats to satisfy his soul." [*Proverbs* 13] The main intent of eating is the inner, spiritual effect. [*Or Ha-Chayim,* Vayera]

A hint of this secret is found in the comparison to the Temple altar and the burning of the sacrifices, as it says, "... to be a fire-offering of pleasing fragrance to the L-rd." [*Numbers* 28:1-8]

The Recanti agrees, likewise, that there is a great secret hidden in the story of the angels who visited Abraham, as discussed also by his teacher, Nachmanides (the Rambam). The supernal fire descended to consume the food, like a sacrifice on the altar. [*Recanti,* Vayera] The smoke and the fragrance of the sacrifice ascends to G-d, and likewise, with the food we eat in the proper manner. [*Chesed l'Avraham,* Nahar 45] When we consume food, energy is released, similar to the burning of a sacrifice, and we hope to use the energy gained from this food as an offering to G-d. Deeper explanations can be found in our mystical writings.

The angels wished to be like humans and to offer their physical food to G-d, but they failed. The Midrash explains that they mixed milk and meat as they ate, which is forbidden by Jewish law. G-d chastised them, saying that you, who often criticize the Jewish people and object to having given them the Torah, transgressed something that every Jewish school child knows, that we do not eat together milk and meat! And the angels had no words to defend their actions. [Midrash *Tehillim*]


## FEAST OF THE RIGHTEOUS

The Holy One, blessed be He, has promised to make a giant celebration feast for the righteous during the Messianic times in the World-to-Come, as one of their great rewards for living a holy life. [Talmud, *Pesachim* 119b] Most of our sages teach us that this will be an actual feast and not just a metaphor for a spiritual occurrence. [*Zohar,* Toldos] Of course, there will be phenomenal spiritual revelations at this meal which the world has never known, but our concerns here are the unusual nutritional aspects. Rabbi Moshe Maimon (the Rambam, Maimonides), though, believes the feast for the righteous is not a physical meal, but rather a spiritual phenomenon. [*Yad ha-Chazakah,* Hilchos Teshuva 8:6]

Our sages teach us that this great feast will consist of preserved wine (yayin ha-meshumar) together with a meal of the giant fish Livyatan and the wild ox (shor ha-bar, behemoth). The Talmud teaches that in the World-to-Come there will be a revelation of something which "no eye has ever seen." This refers to the ancient, holy preserved wine, which is guarded by G-d in its original grapes from the six days of Creation until the time when it will be revealed. [Talmud, *Brochos* 34b] Drinking from this wine will be one of the great rewards for the righteous in the World-to-Come. Those who merit to drink from this special wine will experience a level of joyousness which has never been experienced throughout the history of mankind, and both man and G-d will rejoice in ecstatic bliss. [Talmud, *Sanhedrin* 79a]

This special wine, from the first grapes of Creation, has the elevated quality of having its origins in the Creation of the world, when G-d created "something" from "absolute nothingness." [*Maharsha*, Talmud, *Brochos 34b*] All grapes which ever existed in the world and which will grow in the future all have their origins in these original grapes from which the preserved wine was produced. All the wine we drink today has its source in this original wine. For this reason it is to be guarded from use for unholy purposes, and has such high spiritual importance according to Jewish tradition. [*Sefer Tzioni al ha-Torah*, Ha'azinu]

To broaden our grasp, everything we eat has its connection to the foods of the six days of Creation! Think about it. The seeds of the coming generations are contained in our present foods. The vitalizing force (giving life to all things) is passed down from the Creator and carried by the seeds in all foods, and in all living things (Man), from generation to generation, in an unbroken chain from the six days of Creation to the present time, to continue on and on. Seeds, then, are the vehicle, carrying the life force throughout the Creation.

In the World-to-Come, when the righteous will rejoice with a special feast, the world will return to its original source with the drinking of the preserved wine. After this feast, the world will come full circle, and our nourishment will return to the fully-formed cakes which will grow on the trees and from fruits, as in the first times in the Garden of Eden.

Returning to our topic, the feast of the righteous, we have learned that there will also be served special fish and meat at this banquet. Regarding the fish, the Talmud teaches us that Rav Yehudah said in the name of Rav:

> Everything that G-d created in His world, He created
> male and female. Even Leviathan the straight serpent and
> Leviathan the crooked serpent (giant fish or sea monsters)
> He created male and female; and were they to cohabit with
> each other, they would destroy the entire world. What
> did G-d do? He castrated the male, killed the female and
> salted her for the righteous in the World-to-Come, as it
> says, "He shall slay the tannin that is in the sea." [Talmud,
> *Bava Basra* 74b]

The Talmud continues that on the fifth day of Creation, as well, G-d created the land monsters, Behemoth, or the wild ox (Shor Ha-bar). Likewise, if they had mated they also would have destroyed the whole world. So, G-d castrated the male and cooled the female and preserved it for the righteous for the World-to-Come.

The Midrash teaches that in the Messianic times there will be a massive battle between the wild ox (Shor Ha-bar) and the fish Livyatan. The ox will batter the Livyatan with its horns and rend it, and the Livyatan will smash the ox with its fins and pierce through it. [Midrash, *Vayikra Raba* 13:3]

So, after drinking from the ancient preserved wine, the righteous will dine on the Livyatan fish and on the meat of the ox at this special feast.

Together with the other participants, the Talmud teaches us that our Patriarchs will also be present and will rejoice. And after all the festivity there will be a discussion regarding who will lead the "Grace after Meals." [Talmud, *Pesachim* 119b] Ultimately, King David will be chosen as the most appropriate, and then he will proclaim:

> I will raise the cup of salvation, and call upon the name
> of the L-rd. ... and everyone will achieve complete
> knowledge and will be joyous. [*Psalms* 116:13]

Ultimately, when we pass from our worldly material existence and enter a more spiritual realm in the World-to-Come, then we shall join the angels in their manner of eating. We shall be nourished from the most spiritual, heavenly manna, and we shall bathe in the radiance of the Divine Presence, like the angels.

# Section III

# Eating Well

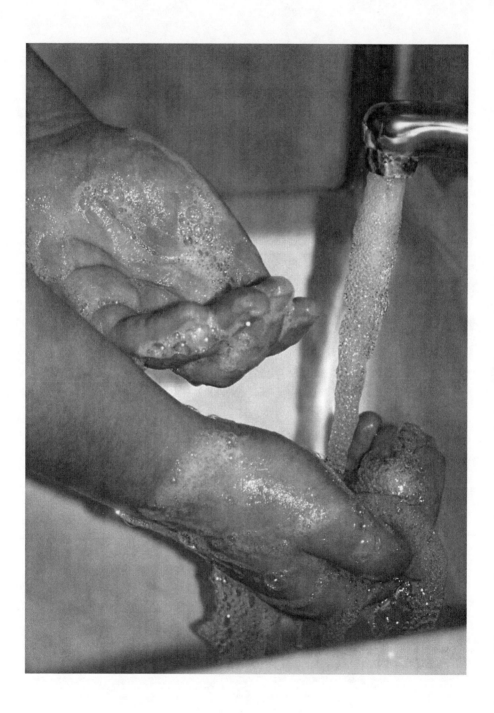

# Chapter 10

## Food Blessings and Relaxed Eating

How wonderful it is that the Creator provides us with foods to nourish ourselves. According to Jewish custom, we do not eat or drink until we praise the Almighty.

We ask permission, in a sense, from the Creator of the world, before partaking of His Creation. Upon reciting a blessing on a particular food or drink, (even without our awareness of its occurrence) we release the sparks of holiness, and at times, souls contained in these foods, allowing them to ascend to a higher spiritual level. All of this is explained more fully in our mystical writings.

The spiritual components of the Creation are in a constant flux of elevation, progressing from one spiritual level to the next until they return to their source. With regard to eating, minerals from the ground enter plants which may have their elevation when eaten by an animal or human. These sparks of holiness from both the plant which was eaten by the animal, and the sparks in the animal itself, may have a further elevation and rectification when eaten by a human, who uses the energy and nutrients gained from these foods for a holy purpose.

With all of these wonderful things going on, of course we want to be part of this and to aid in the elevation of the sparks in the foods and of ourselves, through reciting blessings over the various foods before eating.

Our rabbis have specified special blessings for each particular food and drink which are the most appropriate praise of the Creator, and which can best release and elevate the sparks of holiness contained in each food. A detailed accounting of these various blessings is beyond the scope of this text, but some examples will be given to wet your appetite! A more thorough explanation may be found in the "Code of Jewish Law" (Shulchan Aruch), or by consulting a qualified rabbi to learn the proper recitation of the many blessings, to ensure the maximal praise of the Creator.

Before eating a meal containing bread, it is customary to wash our hands from a vessel and to recite the following blessing:

> "Blessed are You, L-rd our G-d, King of the Universe,
> who has sanctified us with His commandments, and
> commanded us concerning the washing of the hands."

After drying the hands the following blessing is recited before eating the bread and beginning the meal:

> "Blessed are You, L-rd our G-d, King of the Universe, who
> brings forth bread from the earth."

After finishing our meal, it is customary to recite various blessings to give additional thanks to G-d for the benefit that we obtain from the food. After completing a meal including bread, which has extra importance according to our rabbis, we recite a moving set of blessings, composed from various sources.

Our teacher Moses was inspired with the special hazan blessing, when he first saw the manna begin to fall in the Sinai desert after our escape from Egyptian bondage. [Talmud, *Brochos 48 b*] This blessing was thereafter continually recited after Jews ate their daily manna portion in the wilderness, and was later included by our rabbis as the first blessing after a meal where bread is eaten. This beautiful blessing reads, as follows:

> "Blessed are You, L-rd our G-d, King of the Universe, who,
> in His goodness, provides sustenance for the entire world
> with grace, with kindness and with mercy. He gives food
> to all flesh, for His kindness is everlasting. Through His
> great goodness to us continuously we do not lack [food],
> and may we never lack food, for the sake of His great
> Name. For He, benevolent G-d, provides nourishment and
> sustenance for all, does good to all, and prepares food for
> all His creatures whom He has created, as it is said: You
> open Your hand and satisfy the desire of every living thing.
> Blessed are You L-rd, who provides food for all."

Apart from a meal containing bread, if a food containing one or more of the five species of grain grown in the Land of Israel (wheat, barley, oats, rye or spelt) if they were boiled or ground and made into a dish, the following blessing is recited:

"Blessed are You, L-rd our G-d, King of the Universe, who creates the various kinds of foods."

A special blessing over wine, which is considered the holiest of drinks, is recited:

"Blessed are You, L-rd our G-d, King of the Universe, who creates the fruit of the vine."

The following blessing is recited on fruits, whose importance was discussed in the chapter on Tu b'Shevat:

"Blessed are You, L-rd our G-d, King of the Universe, who creates the fruit of the tree."

The blessing on vegetables is:

"Blessed are You, L-rd our G-d, King of the Universe, who creates the fruit of the earth."

The blessing over milk, fish, meat, eggs, cheese and all liquids (except wine and grape juice) is:

"Blessed are You, L-rd our G-d, King of the Universe, by whose word all things came to be."

These are an important sample of the many wonderful food blessings recited before or after consuming various foods and drink to praise the Creator for His kindness in providing us with the foods we need.

## HAND WASHING AND FOOD HYGIENE

Ritual washing of the hands was derived by the Rabbis of the Talmud from practices in the ancient Temple in Jerusalem. These practices were based on various verses in the Hebrew Bible.

The Hebrew term for ritual hand washing is netilat yadayim, which means "lifting up of the hands." Jewish law requires that the water used for ritual washing be pure, unused, and not discolored. The water must be poured from a large cup or vessel. Generally, water is poured on each hand, covering the hand to the wrist, three times on each hand. When first arising in the morning the hands are washed three times, alternating the hands between each washing. At meals, before eating bread, the hands are washed with various customs. One common custom is to hold a two-handled vessel in the left hand, washing the right hand completely three times. Then the vessel is transferred to the right hand, and the left hand is washed three times. The hands are then raised and the following blessing is recited:

> "Blessed are You, L-rd our G-d, King of the Universe,
> who has sanctified us with His commandments, and
> commanded us concerning the washing of the hands."

The hands are then dried well, and then the blessing over the bread is recited:

> "Blessed are You, L-rd our G-d, King of the Universe, who
> brings forth bread from the earth."

The bread is then dipped in salt, reminiscent of the Temple altar where salt was always used with the offerings, and then eaten. After the meal the fingertips are generally washed, as well.

Hand washing is required after visiting the restroom, and whenever a part of the body which is usually covered is touched, as a measure of cleanliness. As well, hand washing is required when touching an unclean item such as one's shoes, an insect or animal, or after visiting a cemetery or having contact with a corpse. The hands are washed before prayer, after cutting one's hair or nails, after touching one's scalp, or the inside of the nose or ears.

In general, then, Judaism emphasizes the importance of cleanliness, and of clean hands and a pure heart. Besides the spiritual benefits, many health benefits may also be gained by such practices. During the Black Plague in Italy in 1386 C.E., the Jews had far less casualties than the general population. It is believed that the Jewish practice of extensive hand washing had a significant impact on their survival.

Food hygiene is not the reason behind the kosher laws, as explained in Chapter 3. Nevertheless, there may be significant health benefits. There are strict prohibitions against eating most insects, so food must be bug-free. People inspect their vegetables, fruits, and grains very carefully, and storage conditions must be on a very clean level.

## RELAXED EATING

A very important part of eating well is not just what we eat but also *how* we eat! It is best to take meals and snacks at the same time every day, in a relaxed, positive setting. Avoid skipping meals, especially breakfast, as doing so will weaken your body. Going for long periods of time without adequate nutrition leads to fatigue, low blood sugar, loss of concentration, headaches, and increased stress.

Stress, from whatever source, is very damaging to the digestion. The stomach and neck tense up after hearing bad news or during aggravating discussions full of complaints and negativity. Can you feel yourself tensing as you picture this?

Now relax, and learn to relax before, during, and after eating. It is a good idea to relax more during your entire day, to ensure your continued good health.

Sit with a good posture. Slow down. Do not gobble up your food as if you have not eaten for days. Try to have positive conversations and happy thoughts during your meals. Make meal times happy times.

Relaxing before eating will improve your digestion, allowing your digestive glands (the parotids and the sublinguals) to produce the necessary digestive enzymes. To help yourself relax you may wish to try a progressive relaxation technique or some deep breathing. Imagine your stomach muscles relaxing, and they will relax. Release all tension from your body, and clear your mind. Repeat a positive statement over and over to yourself, either mentally or aloud. Tell yourself that you are relaxed and ready to begin eating in a healthy way. A prayer said before eating will make you fully aware of Who is in ultimate control, and Who has graciously provided the food you are about to enjoy.

Eat slowly, and chew your food thoroughly. Digestion begins in the mouth, with each well-chewed bite. Limit fluids during meals to one small glass, and drink ample fluids between meals (6 to 8 glasses per day). In this way you will not dilute the essential digestive juices of the mouth and stomach. Slowing down the pace of eating will also help you avoid overeating.

## JEWISH FOOD TRADITIONS – FAMILY, FRIENDS, COMMUNITY

Judaism emphasizes togetherness. A Jew is never alone, as tradition teaches us that G-d is always with each and every person. In addition, the family unit is extremely important in Jewish life, and all of the weekly Sabbath and holiday meals and celebrations center around the family. Two outstanding meals during the year are the Purim seuda, Hebrew for "meal," and the Passover seder. The meals generally center around bread, as these blessings have great religious significance. Meat and wine are often served, as well, at Jewish food celebrations due to their importance. A l'chaim (Hebrew for "to life") toast generally highlights a Jewish food celebration.

Friends and family gather for festival meals throughout one's lifetime. A meal is served after circumcision of a new son, and a kiddush food celebration with wine and cake and other goodies is given on Sabbath morning after the prayers in the synagogue to celebrate the birth of a new daughter. Food celebrations mark the reaching of age thirteen, Bar Mitzvah, in boys and age twelve, Bat Mitzvah, in girls, where they are first obligated according to Jewish law to observe religious precepts or mitzvoth in Hebrew.

The wedding celebration of family, friends and the entire community again involves elaborate, festive meals with music and dancing. In religious homes the wedding celebration continues each evening for seven days, with a festive meal in honor of the bride and groom at the homes of family or friends.

When study of a tractate of the Talmud is completed, again a festive meal is partaken by friends and family.

There are community meal celebrations, as well. In the Hassidic world, the leader, referred to as the Grand Rabbi or Rebbe, of each dynasty generally conducts a public meal or tish, which is Yiddish (a Jewish language spoken by many Ashkenizic Jews) for "table." At this gathering of the Rebbe and his followers, who are known as hassidim, come together on the Sabbath and holidays, or sometimes to mark a special occasion or anniversary of the passing of a great Torah sage or tzaddik (Hebrew for a righteous person). The tish gives the atmosphere that the hassidim are the invited guests of the Rebbe, who washes his hands for bread and eats various food courses, distributing the leftover foods among the participants. It is considered spiritually beneficial to eat from these foods which have been blessed and partaken by the Rebbe, and there is often much commotion to receive these foods at the tish.  During the course of the meal there is singing and drinking of l'chaim, Hebrew for a toast "to life" from an alcoholic beverage. The Rebbe generally speaks words of Torah, as well to inspire the participants. There is a general feeling of brotherhood and community at the tish, which gives one inspiration and strength for the coming days. A similar event occurs in the Lubavitcher Hassidic community, and it is known as a farbrengen.

## SPECIAL FOOD CUSTOMS

There is some variety according to custom, or minhag in Hebrew, of the various food choices among the different groups of Jews today. Much of the differences occur from influences of climate or surrounding non-Jewish traditional foods in the various locations in the world where Jews have lived.

Ashkenazic foods tend to be heavier, reflecting the cold environments where these Jews generally lived. They typically include heavy meats and fatty foods, as well as potatoes, buckwheat, and root vegetables like carrots or beets. Sephardic foods are generally lighter, having their origins in warmer climates with leaner meats, rice, couscous and legumes, and less heavy, fried foods, though there are exceptions.

There are many Hassidic food customs, also depending upon the origin of the particular Hassidic dynasty, mainly in Eastern Europe. An extra potato or noodle kugel, Yiddish for "pudding," may be served when an extra Torah scroll is taken out from the holy ark and read during the synagogue services at certain times. There is variety among the Sabbath food preparations, as well, among the various Ashkenazic Jews. The chopped balls of fish, known as gefilte fish in Yiddish, for example, generally contain less sugar and are therefore less sweet in families originating in Russia or Poland and are made sweeter in families with roots in Galicia or Hungary. The hot dish set aside before the Sabbath, where cooking is forbidden, on a hotplate and served at the morning meal, is known as chulent, in Yiddish, by Ashkenazic Jews from Russia or Polish roots. It would generally include meat or chicken and potatoes, while Galician Jews may substitute buckwheat for the potatoes. Hungarian Jews would commonly include beans, as well. Sometimes barley is added. Sephardic Jews usually include rice as the carbohydrate source and use lighter meats.

In some families additional personal customs, which have developed over the years or generations are included. Extra traditions and customs based on the mystical aspects of the Torah, known as kabbalah, are observed.

## KOSHER DINING

In the past, a kosher observant Jew generally was restricted to eating with family or friends. Nowadays, as kosher supervision has greatly expanded, Jews observing kashrut are far less limited.

Many kosher restaurants are available throughout the world. The market has grown to meet the demand. One web-site has a listing of 2780 restaurants in 50 countries! Most of the restaurants provide kosher foods typical of either Ashkenazic or Sephardic food habits. In Israel Sephardic-style falafel stores are commonplace. Kosher pizza stores abound, as well. World-wide, there are large restaurants for many happy occasions, banquets, family celebrations, and simply, for vacation. Many specialty restaurants, sit-down and take-out, operate throughout the world, offering kosher Italian, Chinese, American, or other gourmet menus at various price ranges.

# Chapter 11

## Natural Cooking and Seasonings

Good nutrition can be ensured by eating a varied diet of fresh, wholesome foods. Nutrients are retained better when the fresh produce is sold locally and in season, avoiding the long delays during transportation and storage. Eating for health is important and can be an exciting discovery experience. Grains, legumes, fresh fruits, and vegetables are the foundation of the diet just as they were in the teachings of the Torah, Talmud, and Rambam.

Explore new foods in supermarkets, local farmers' markets, and natural food shops. By taking the time to try previously unknown, unprocessed foods, you will discover a new eating experience with vibrant food colors, rich flavors, varied textures and, in general, a larger variety of foods. You will relearn the childhood joy of eating crunchy vegetables, and sweet, juicy fruits, as well, as the natural tastes of herbs and spices.

These changes, however, cannot and should not be made overnight. Gradually improving your diet is the best way to ensure good health and long-term change. Begin by reducing high trans fat and saturated fat foods, especially fried foods, chips, fatty meats, and have fewer high-sugar sodas, sweetened juices, candies, sweet snacks, and desserts. If your weight is above normal, reduce the size of your portions and faithfully walk more or find physical work like gardening, cleaning, or pursuing active hobbies each day. Then take one step at a time, progressing to a diet based on grains and legumes with generous amounts of vegetables and fruits, low-fat dairy products, and if you wish, ocean fish, and poultry.

Begin altering your favorite recipes, cooking those you already enjoy in a healthier way. Try to make the same recipe but with less meat. Or, replace the meat with cooked whole grains, beans, or finely chopped vegetables. You will often be able to leave out or reduce the amount of oil without significantly altering the final product. Instead of sautéing in oil or margarine, cook vegetables in a small amount of water and steam them. Add some lemon juice, vegetable stock, or apple cider vinegar to spark the taste. For salad dressings, use olive or canola oil, or as an alternative include vinegars, lemon juice, tomato or orange juice. You can use fresh fruits or natural fruit juice or compotes as your sweetening agents.

## WHOLE GRAINS

| Breads and Cereals |
| --- |
| Barley |
| Brown rice, Cream of Rice, Rice flour |
| Buckwheat (Kasha), Buckwheat flour |
| Bulgar |
| Corn, Cornmeal, Corn flour |
| Millet |
| Oats (rolled, cut), Oat bran |
| Rye, Rye flour |
| Teff |
| Wheat berries, Whole-wheat flour, Wheat germ, Wheat bran |

### Qualities and Preparation of Whole Grains

Grains are the seeds of grasses. Each grain contains a seed (germ), food for the seed (endosperm), and a covering to protect the seed and the food source (hull and bran). Milling and refining remove the germ and bran layers to process the grains into flours. Whole grains, on the other hand, contain all three components: germ, endosperm, and bran. Whole grains therefore contain nutrients – such as more protein, B-vitamins, iron, essential fats, and fiber – that are otherwise removed during the refining process. Use whole-grain breads and cereals, muffins, cakes, crackers, and pastas.

*General Cooking Advice for Grains:*

Combine the grain and the boiling water, cover, reduce heat, and simmer. An optional method that requires longer cooking times but produces a lighter product is as follows:

> Combine the grain and the boiling water and then bring the water again to a strong boil. Cover and turn off the heat. Allow the grain to stand covered for about 1 hour. Note: Do not stir grains while cooking, as this makes them stick together.

*Barley*

Barley has a chewy texture and nutty taste. It looks like rice and expands when cooked. It is useful as a thickener and in soups. To prepare, add 3 parts water to 1 part grain. Bring it to a boil, cover and simmer for 1 hour.

*Brown Rice*

The whole, unpolished rice grain has a nutty, wholesome flavor. Brown rice comes in long- and short-grain varieties. It provides high-quality protein when eaten together with beans. Brown rice is an excellent source of fiber, B-vitamins, and complex carbohydrate. To prepare, add 2 parts water to 1 part grain. Bring it to a boil, cover and simmer for 45 minutes.

*Buckwheat (Kasha)*

This is actually a pyramid-shaped seed of a fruit rather than a true grain. Buckwheat has a rich and earthy flavor. Use it as a grain in cooked dishes. To prepare, dry roast it. You may coat the grains with a small amount of oil and stir while roasting. Then add boiling water, 2 parts water to 1 part grain. Cover and cook for 20 minutes.

### Bulgur

Bulgur is cracked wheat that has been precooked and then dried. It has a nutty flavor and fluffy texture. To prepare, add 2 parts boiling water to 1 part grain. Cover and let it stand for 20 minutes.

### Corn

Corn kernels have a nutritional content similar to that of other grains. Cornmeal can be used to make cereals and muffins. Corn can be popped to produce popcorn.

### Millet

Millet is a delicate, nutty-tasting grain that looks like tiny yellow beads. Dry roasting or sautéing in oil is optional. To prepare, add 2½ parts water to 1 part grain. Bring to a boil, cover and simmer for 30 minutes. Remove from the heat and uncover.

### Oats

Oat flakes and oat bran, famous for their cholesterol-lowering action, can be used as a cereal and may be added to cookies, muffins, and breads. Rolled oats are used in granola mixes. To cook, add 3 parts boiling water to 1 part cereal. Simmer until done.

### Wheat Berries

Each berry is one whole wheat kernel. This is a very hard grain which, when cooked, has a chewy texture and a sweet flavor. Wheat berries may be sprouted, cracked, or eaten whole. To cook, add 3 parts water to 1 part grain. Bring to a boil, cover and simmer until done.

## LEGUMES

| Peas and Beans |
|---|
| Azuki beans |
| Chickpeas (Garbanzos) |
| Lentils (brown, orange, green) |
| Kidney beans |
| Mung beans |
| Peanuts |
| Soybeans, Soy flour, Soy milk, Tofu |
| Split peas (green, yellow) |
| White beans (navy, lima) |

### Qualities and Preparation of Legumes

Beans and peas are a good source of protein and other nutrients. Eaten together with grains, they are an excellent substitute for meat (free of cholesterol and saturated fat) and are even effective in reducing bad LDL-cholesterol!

Use them for soups and stews and cook and sprinkle them on salads. Mash them after cooking for dips and sandwich spreads, and use them together with vegetables. Season them with garlic and onions or add herbs or spices.

To remove the gas-producing, indigestible carbohydrate that sticks to the outer skin of legumes, soak the peas or beans overnight in the refrigerator in a bowl of water. Rinse and then cook in fresh water. Legumes must be boiled in plenty of water for a long period of time, at least 1½ hours, until soft. It's a good idea to begin with small servings of legumes and increase amounts gradually over weeks, thereby allowing your body to produce the digestive enzymes needed to properly digest beans and peas.

### Chickpeas (Garbanzo Beans)

These are large, round, beige beans with a nutty taste. Use chickpeas in salads, soups, and as a spread.

### Lentils

These come in several varieties as small brown-, orange-, or green-colored beans. Use them in soups or salads. They can also be mixed with grains.

### Kidney Beans

These beans are red and kidney-shaped. Use them in salads, stews, and soups.

### Soybeans

These are small, yellow beans that contain more protein than any other vegetable source. Soy products, which are more easily digested than soy beans, include soy flour, soy milk, soy sauce, and tofu (bean curd or soy cheese).

### Split Peas

Split peas have a hearty flavor and come in green and yellow varieties. They taste great in soups or may be eaten with whole grains.

### White Beans

These are white, middle-sized beans. Use them in stews, salads, and soups. They combine nicely with tomatoes or with tomato sauce and herbs.

## VEGETABLES

| Raw or Cooked Vegetables | | |
|---|---|---|
| Artichokes | Horseradish | Pumpkin |
| Asparagus | Kale | Radishes |
| Beets | Kohlrabi | Red cabbage |
| Broccoli | Leeks | Scallions |
| Cabbage | Lettuce | Spinach |
| Carrots | Mint | Sprouts (all kinds) |
| Cauliflower | Mushrooms | Squashes |
| Celery | Onions | String beans |
| Corn | Parsley | Sweet potatoes |
| Cucumbers | Parsnips | Tomatoes |
| Eggplant | Peppers | Turnips |
| Garlic | Potatoes | |

Vegetables are an important source of vitamins, minerals, and phyto-nutrients. They are especially good sources of vitamins A and C and also supply riboflavin, folacin, iron, and magnesium. Due to their high fiber content, vegetables are filling while remaining low in calories.

### Steaming Vegetables

Steam vegetables to retain their color and texture, and their water-soluble vitamins. Put the vegetables on a stainless-steel steamer above 1-2 inches (2-4 cm.) of water in a covered saucepan. Bring the water to a boil and reduce the heat. Steam covered for the least amount of time necessary, which varies according to the type of vegetable being prepared.

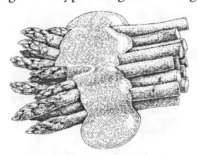

**Sprouts**

Use alfalfa seeds, mung beans, lentils, soybeans, wheat berries, or sunflower seeds to make your sprouts. The only equipment you really need is a flat baking dish covered with a towel. Sprouts will provide you with variety in eating. Their proteins are in a simpler form than those in the unsprouted beans or seeds and are therefore more digestible.

| Making Sprouts | |
|---|---|
| Day 1 | Soak ¼ cup seeds or beans in 1 cup of water in a dish or a jar for at least 10 hours. |
| Day 2 | Drain the water from the seeds or beans and rinse well with cold water. Place them in a single layer on a wide flat dish. Cover with a damp layer of paper towels; cover the dish with a towel. (Alternate method: Place the seeds or beans in a jar. Cover the mouth of the jar with cheesecloth attached with a rubber band or with a sprouting lid. Wrap the jar in a towel and rest it on its side.)<br><br>Rinse the seeds or beans thoroughly twice a day with cool water. After rinsing, cover the seeds or beans, in a dish, with a paper towel and a dish towel. |
| Days 3-5 | Continue rinsing twice a day. Most sprouts will be ready by day 4. The sprouts should be at least 2-3 times the length of the initial seed or bean. Refrigerate in plastic bags for up to a week. Daily rinsing of sprouts with cool water, allowing all the water to drain off, will preserve their freshness and will extend their storage life. Do not eat moldy sprouts. |

**FRUITS**

| Fresh Fruits | | |
|---|---|---|
| Apples | Guava | Papaya |
| Apricots | Kiwi | Peaches |
| Bananas | Kumquats | Pears |
| Berries | Lemons | Persimmons |
| Cactus | Loquats | Pineapple |
| Cherries | Mandarin oranges | Plums |
| Dates | Mango | Pomegranates |
| Figs | Melons | Strawberries |
| Grapefruit | Nectarines | Tangerines |
| Grapes | Oranges | Watermelon |
| Dried Fruits | | |
| Apricots | Figs | Prunes |
| Dates | Papaya | Raisins |
| Fruit Juices | | |
| Apple | Grapefruit | Peach |
| Apricot | Mango | Pineapple |
| Grape | Orange | Prune |

Fruits are excellent sources of vitamins A and C, fiber, phytonutrients, and potassium. They can be consumed raw, as juice, dried, lightly cooked, or even baked. Choose from a wide variety as they appear in their seasons, and enjoy!

## ANIMAL PRODUCTS

There are wonderful nutrients, flavors, tastes, and textures in animal products like fish, lean meats, dairy products, and eggs. They are high in proteins, many minerals and vitamins, and healthy fatty acids like omega-3s. Animal products are healthiest for human consumption when they are free from contaminants (pollutants in ocean and lake water for fish), medications (like antibiotics or hormones), and when their diets consist of more natural foods, which are normal for that species (like offering vegetarian feed to chickens).

Animal products are often high in fat or they are served with added fat from frying, gravies, sauces, marinades and the like. It is more healthy to serve meats and fish broiled, boiled, roasted, baked, and grilled where the fat drains off and the meat does not cook in its own juices. Dairy products like yogurt, cheeses, and milk can be included in a healthy diet and they are available in lower fat varieties. Animal products should be served modest in size, and if you have a weight problem, portions should be smaller than you used to eat.

Egg yolks contain cholesterol, but whites, which contain no fat or cholesterol, may be eaten unrestrictedly and may be used in cooking and baking. On the other hand, studies at Harvard Medical School have shown that consumption of up to one egg a day is unlikely to have substantial overall impact on the risk of coronary heart disease or stroke among healthy men and women.[1]

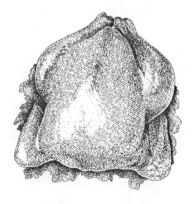

## OILS

We must consume a limited amount of fat on a regular basis in order to obtain fat soluble vitamins and the essential fatty acids. The oils most recommended are cold-pressed olive or canola, as these are highest in mono-unsaturated fats, which today are considered most heart-healthy. About a tablespoon or two a day is all we need. Alternative oils that may be used on occasion include safflower, corn, soy, sunflower, and sesame. With these oils, as well, the cold-pressed varieties are recommended, as the heat extract method converts these oils to a less healthy form.

To form a stable, solid fat such as margarine, the food industry often adds hydrogen to unsaturated fats, to produce a more solid product. To these foods, hydrogen atoms can be added either in the "cis" or in the "trans" position (with each hydrogen on opposite sides of the double bond). Nutritionists recommend reduced consumption of trans fats. Major sources of trans fatty acids include processed foods: partially hydrogenated margarine, shortening, commercial frying fats, and high-fat bakery products.

The fatty acids in dietary fat, consist of three main types, classified according to their chemical composition, namely saturated, monounsaturated (MUFA) and polyunsaturated fatty acids (PUFA). PUFA are further subdivided into two types according to the position of the double bonds in the molecule, either omega-3 found more in plant life or omega-6 from animal protein and from oils extracted from grains, such as corn and safflower oils. Many nutritionists today consider the modern diet unbalanced, overly rich in omega-6 fatty acids.

Scientific studies have shown that omega-3 fats may help prevent coronary artery disease, high blood pressure, and other diseases with inflammatory or autoimmune components. [2,3] Since the current intakes of omega-3 fats are low, nutritionists encourage increased intakes of omega-3 food sources, like salmon and sardines, for example, and plant sources such as ground flaxseed and oil, canola oil, and nuts, especially walnuts.

## NUTS

> I went down into the garden of nuts to see the fruits of the
> valley...[*Song of Songs* 6:11]

The Jewish people are likened to the nut. The Torah commentator Rashi explains that just as a nut from the outside appearance is totally wood and its inner content is not revealed, so the Jewish people are full of modest deeds and wisdom which are not always externally apparent. [Rashi, *Song of Songs* 6:11]

Interestingly, the numerical equivalent (gematria), of the Hebrew word for "nut" (egoz) is 17, the same as the Hebrew word for "sin" (chet). Many, therefore, have the custom to avoid eating nuts on the Jewish New Year (Rosh ha-Shana), which is a time of great judgment.

Nuts have four shells or husks: the outer husk, which is hard and bitter, dries up and falls off; next comes an outer hard shell; a more inner shell which separates between parts of the food; and a thin, inner membrane which covers the nut itself and can be eaten together with the nut.

### The Walnut and Its Four Shells:

Thin inner membrane
Thick inner shell
Hard outer shell
Outer husk dries up and falls off

The four shells or "husks" in Torah literature have mystical connotations. In short, the side opposite to holiness, the klipot (translated as "husks"), or the "bad," is symbolized by the nut shells. These surround or attach themselves to the holiness, or "good," like the nut shells which surround the edible portion. After removing the four "husks" or shells, we arrive at the nut itself, or essence, which is divided into four parts. The nut reveals the life force, or the supernal flow of vitality, which is contained and hidden in the tree from which it grows. And in general, all fruits are revelations of a hidden vital force which each tree has received from the source of life, from G-d.

**Nutritional Aspects**

Any oily seed kernel or fruit found within a shell and used as a food may be regarded as a nut, though botanically, this is not always the case. Nuts are highly prized for their high oil content, and they are a source of healthy fats. They are used in cooking, eaten raw, sprouted, or roasted, and they are pressed for oil that is used in cooking. They are also used as nut spreads, such as peanut butter, almond butter, etc. Nuts, both tree nuts and peanuts (which are actually legumes) are among the most common food allergens.

Some commonly used examples are listed:

| | | |
|---|---|---|
| Almonds | Brazil Nuts | Hazelnuts |
| Cashews | Pistachios | Macadamia Nuts |
| Walnuts | | |

Though nuts are a high-fat food, they are mostly heart-healthy with essential fatty acids, linoleic and linolenic, which are important for growth, physical and mental development, healthy skin and hair, control of blood pressure, immune response and blood clotting.[4,5] The fats in nuts are mostly unsaturated, especially rich in monounsaturated fat. Nuts are also a rich natural source of vitamin E, an antioxidant, and are significant sources of protein, dietary fiber, magnesium, copper, phosphorus, potassium, selenium and folate.[4,5] Walnuts are especially high in omega-3.[6]

Several epidemiological studies have shown that people who eat nuts regularly are less likely to suffer from coronary heart disease.[5-8] Nuts contain various cardio-protective  substances, including their omega-3 content. Clinical trials have found that eating various nuts such as almonds and walnuts can actually lower serum LDL cholesterol.[6]

Seeds may be used to add variety, texture, and flavor:  poppy seeds, sesame seeds, sunflower seeds, and sprouted seeds.

## SAUCES, DRESSINGS, AND TOPPINGS

Sauces are traditionally high in fat, made with plenty of butter, flour, oil, and eggs. Alternative ideas, using healthier thickening agents – such as cornstarch, whole-grain flours, and pureed vegetables and legumes – will add variety and palatability to your vegetables and grains. A successful sauce or dressing can turn a plain salad, or fruit, grain or pasta dish into a gourmet's delight and can be the saving factor for many in the pursuit of a healthy nutritional lifestyle.

## OTHER NUTRITIONAL FACTORS

Recently, there is an increased awareness of various additional nutritional factors in our foods which may have a positive affect on our health.

### Phytochemicals

Plants provide color, aroma, and flavor and include pigments such as flavonoids, carotenoids, and anthocyanins. Plant foods, besides containing major nutrients such as protein, fat, carbohydrates, fiber, vitamins and minerals, also have large numbers of non-nutrient compounds called phytochemicals. Dietary sources of phytochemicals include fruits, vegetables, legumes, whole grains, nuts, seeds, herbs and spices. Phytochemicals are biologically active, naturally existing substances in plants that show potential for reducing risk for cancer and heart disease in humans.[9,10]

### Probiotics

Probiotics is the name given to live bacteria that are either foods or are added to foods in adequate amounts to repopulate the intestine and to confer a beneficial health effect. The most common probiotics include lactobacillus organisms and bifidobacteria. Research has suggested that probiotic bacteria may help reduce the incidence or decrease the duration of certain diarrheal illnesses, assist lactose intolerant people with lactose digestion, and may enhance immune function.[11]

The rationale for probiotics is that the body's normal intestine contains a mixture of trillions of bacteria (several pounds in weight) comprised of hundreds of species referred to as the gut flora. The amount and variety of these bacterial types can be put out of balance by a wide range of events including the use of antibiotics or other medications, poor diet, excess alcohol, stress, and illness. In these cases, the bacteria that work well with our bodies may decrease in number, allowing harmful competitors to thrive to the detriment of our health. There is controversy about probiotic function and true effects, but there is evidence that probiotics do form beneficial temporary colonies which allow the natural flora time to recover from depletion. They help maintain intestinal health by inhibiting overgrowth of harmful bacteria or yeast through competition for attachment sites and nutrients.

Despite their usual benign profile, probiotics may have pathogenic potential in certain populations where there is compromised immunity or in the elderly, so their use in these groups should be determined by a physician.

## Prebiotics

Prebiotics are indigestible food ingredients that stimulate the growth of beneficial bacteria, such as bifidobacterium, already present in the intestine, that thereby improve one's health. They may also work together with probiotics to give an increased benefit. The prebiotics pass undigested into the large intestine and may include, for example, fructooligosaccharides (FOS) and certain dietary fibers, such as pectin, hemicellulose, and inulin.

Examples of FOS-containing foods are honey, beer, onions, rye, Jerusalem artichokes, bananas, maple sugar, asparagus, and oats. Inulin can be found in chicory root, onions, asparagus, and Jerusalem artichokes. By stimulating the growth of beneficial bacteria, the prebiotics thereby reduce the levels of harmful bacteria in our gastrointestinal tract.

## SEASONING WITH SPICES AND HERBS

Spices and herbs include a great variety of vegetable products with aromatic odors and pungent flavors that can enhance the natural flavor of foods. They may be used to add variety and improve the taste of your meals in preparing special diets. A pinch of herbs and a dash of imagination can turn everyday foods into culinary delights!

Spices are defined as parts of plants – such as the dried seeds, buds, fruit or flower parts, or the bark or roots of plants – usually of tropical origin. Herbs are from the leafy parts of temperate-zone plants.

## GROUPS OF SPICES AND HERBS

| Leaves | | |
|---|---|---|
| Basil | Dill Weed | Rosemary |
| Bay Leaf | Marjoram | Sage |
| Chervil | Mint | Savory |
| Chives | Oregano | Tarragon |
| Coriander (Cilantro) | Parsley | Thyme |
| Fruits | | |
| Allspice | Clove | Red Pepper |
| Black Pepper | Mace | Vanilla Bean |
| Caper | Paprika | White Pepper |
| Seeds | | |
| Anise | Coriander Seed | Mustard |
| Caraway | Cumin | Nutmeg |
| Cardamom | Dill Seed | Poppy Seed |
| Celery Seed | Fennel | Sesame Seed |
|  | Fenugreek |  |
| Bulbs and Roots | | |
| Garlic | Ginger | Turmeric |
|  | Onion |  |
| Bark | | |
|  | Cinnamon (cassia) |  |

(Partial listing of spices and herbs prepared by the USDA, Washington, D.C.)

**Herbal Hints**

Spices and herbs should be stored in a cool, dry place in airtight containers. Chop, cut, or crush fresh herbs to release their flavors. Experiment with herbs by increasing the amount to suit your personal taste.

Generally, if a recipe is not available, one should start with ⅛ of a teaspoon of powdered herbs, ¼ of a teaspoon of dried herbs or 1 teaspoon of chopped, fresh herbs when preparing a dish that makes 4 to 6 servings.

Never use herbs to season every dish at one meal. It is better to use caution and start with limited amounts of herbs and spices, until you are familiar with their powers, rather than take a reckless approach. The best cooks use herbs with discretion. They must be used sparingly or they will overpower, rather than enhance, the natural flavors of foods.

*PARSLEY*

*ROSEMARY*

*BASIL*

*MINT*

| Suggestions for Using Herbs and Spices | |
|---|---|
| Anise seed | Cookies, cakes, breads, candy, cheese, beverages, pickles, beef stew, stewed fruits, fish |
| Basil | Tomatoes, noodles, rice, beef stew, meat loaf, fish, vegetable salad, eggplant, potatoes, eggs, carrots, spinach, peas, cheese, jelly |
| Bay leaf | Soups, pickles, fish, meat roasts |
| Caraway seed | Green beans, beets, cabbage, carrots, cauliflower, potatoes, sauerkraut, turnips, zucchini, beef stew, cake, cookies, rice, rye bread |
| Celery seed | Potato salad, fruit salad, tomatoes, vegetables, pickles, breads, rolls, egg dishes, meat loaf, stews, soups |
| Cinnamon | Beverages, bakery products, fruits, pickles, beef stews, roast chicken |
| Cloves | Fruits, pickles, baked goods, fish, meat sauces, pot roast, green beans, carrots, sweet potatoes, tomatoes |
| Dill seed | Pickles, pickled beets, salads, sauerkraut, green beans, egg dishes, stews, fish, chicken, breads |
| Fennel seed | Egg dishes, fish, stews, cheese, vegetables, baked apples, pickles, sauerkraut, breads, cakes, cookies |
| Garlic | Tomato dishes, soups, dips, sauces, salads, pickles, meat, poultry, fish, beverages |
| Ginger | Pickles, baked fruits, soups, vegetables, baked products, beef, poultry, fish, beverages, spinach, squash, mushrooms, broccoli, pizza, spaghetti, egg dishes, breads, soups |
| Mint | Punches, tea, vegetables, sauces for desserts |
| Mustard seed | Pickles, potato salad, cabbage, sauerkraut |
| Nutmeg | Hot beverages, puddings, baked products, fruits, chicken, eggs, vegetables, pickles |
| Onion | Dips, soups, stews, meats, fish, poultry, salads, vegetables, cheese dishes, egg dishes, breads, rice dishes |
| Oregano | Tomatoes, pasta sauces, pizza, vegetable soup, egg dishes, cheese dishes, onions, chicken, fish |

| Paprika | Beef, poultry, fish, egg dishes, cheese dishes, vegetables lacking in color, pickles |
| --- | --- |
| Parsley | Soups, breads, tomato and meat sauces, broiled or fried fish, meats, poultry |
| Pepper, black | Meats, poultry, fish, eggs, vegetables, pickles |
| Pepper, white | White or light meats, vegetables |
| Poppy seed | Pie crust, scrambled eggs, fruit compotes, cookies, cakes, breads, noodles; sprinkle on top of fruit, salads, breads, vegetables, cookies, and cakes |
| Rosemary | Beef, poultry, fish, soups, potatoes, cauliflower, spinach, mushrooms, turnips, fruits, breads |
| Sage | Beef, poultry, fish, cheese, sauces, onions, eggplant, lima beans, tomatoes, soups, potatoes |
| Sesame seed | Pies, cakes, cookies, dips; sprinkle on breads, cookies, salads, noodles, soups, and vegetables |
| Thyme | Meat, poultry, fish, vegetables |
| Vanilla | Baked goods, beverages, puddings |

# *References*

1.  Hu FB, Stampfer MJ, et. al., *JAMA,* April 21, 1999, vol. 281, No. 15, p. 1387.

2.  Mozaffarian D, Katan MB, Ascherio A, et.al. Trans fatty acids and cardiovascular disease. *N Engl J Med* 354: 1601-1613, 2006.

3.  Din JN, Newby DE, Flapan AD. Omega 3 fatty acids and cardiovascular disease-fishing for a natural treatment. *BMJ* 328: 30, 2004.

4.  Simopoulos AP. Omega-3 fatty acids in inflammation and autoimmune diseases. *J Amer College Nutr.* 21, 495-505, 2002.

5.  Ueshima H, Stamler J, Elliott P, et.al. Food omega-3 fatty acid intake of individuals (total, linolenic acid, long-chain) and their blood pressure. *Hypertension.* 50: 313, 2007.

6.  Fukuda J, Ito H, Yoshida T. Antioxidative polyphenols from walnuts. *Phytochemistry.* 63 (7), 795-801, 2003.

7.  Kelly JH Jr, Sabate J. Nuts and coronary heart disease: an epidemiological perspective. *Br J Nutr.* 96 suppl 2: 561-7, 2006.

8.  Sabate J, Oda K, Ros E. Nut consumption and blood lipid levels. *Arch Intern Med.* 170(9), 821-827, 2010.

9.  Steinmetz K, Potter J. Vegetables, fruit, and cancer prevention: a review. *J Am Diet Assoc.* 96: 1037, 1996.

10. Lampe J. Health effects of vegetables and fruit: assessing mechanisms of action in human experimental studies. *Am J Clin Nutr.* 70 [suppl 3]: 475, 1999.

11. Teitelbaum JE, Walker WA. Nutritional impact of pre- and probiotics as protective gastrointestinal organism. *Ann Rev Nutr.* 22: 255, 2002.

# Chapter 12

# Guidelines for Natural Jewish Nutrition

"You are what you eat." Let's expand this well-known expression and consider, "You are what and *the way* you eat."

Our eating style reflects and affects who and what we are. It identifies our approach to life. If we examine various societies and cultures, we see that each has its traditional foods and food ceremonies. "I am Italian; I often eat spaghetti, lasagna, and pizza." "I am a real American; I eat hamburgers, hot dogs, steak, Coke, and French fries." The French eat crepes, Belgians eat waffles, Chinese eat rice, Ethiopians eat teff, Swiss eat chocolate, Israelis eat falafel, and Eskimos eat whale blubber. It reflects and often determines our world view, our values, and our entire approach to life.

"You are the way you eat." Foods are much more than just a collection of nutrients; they are a wealth of influences and connotations. Rare foods and spices are treasured as special culinary delights. Some foods are worshiped in various cultures as having an unusual holiness or are avoided altogether. The type of food we choose can affect our moods. Hot, spicy, or stimulating foods may influence many of us toward hot-temperedness or nervousness. Cooling foods can relax us and give us peace of mind. Foods can help us celebrate and can comfort us when we mourn. They are a sign of love and are a means of uniting people on many occasions.

The various religions use foods to connote their special approach to life. When taken to an extreme, the foods themselves can become the main ritual and one can lose all perspective. Foods may even be worshiped as all-powerful and as the giver of life. This approach to eating is not the Jewish way.

What is your identity? Remember, the "way you eat" (and dress and speak) reveals how you identify yourself. As a Jew, you do not have to imitate others to obtain your identity. Instead, examine your own special, ancient Jewish roots.

We, as Jews, have special G-d-given food habits followed faithfully by most Jews for thousands of years. This food system is based on the rules of kashrus, with a separation of milk- and meat-containing foods. There are many other special details involved in our system of eating which have been previously discussed.

The "way we eat" as Jews is an important part of our heritage and spans from simple rules of common eating etiquette to complex kabbalistic combinations of the Creator's Divine Name (kavannos) concentrated upon while eating. We make a blessing over our food before and after eating, and thank the Almighty for His wonderful kindness which enables us to eat and to continue our lives for His service.

Traditional Jewish dishes have many important cultural and religious connotations. Nevertheless, those of us choosing to follow a healthier, lighter style of eating can find a firm foundation for natural nutrition in the 800-year-old writings of the Rambam, Rabbi Moshe ben Maimon. One of the foremost preventive-health advocates of all time, the Rambam prescribed a synthesis of good health and a nutritional lifestyle reflecting and deepening our connection to our own Jewish roots.

It is with this orientation that I have developed my own approach to natural nutrition, striving to combine a system for healthy living and eating with a strong connection to our important Jewish heritage. I only pray that with the Creator's help, I have been successful.

## GUIDE TO GOOD EATING

As discussed in Chapter 1, after the destruction of the Second Jerusalem Temple, Jews scattered throughout the world for over 2000 years. Their eating patterns often reflected the climates and the regional food customs of their places of residence over the generations. With migration of Jewish populations there has been a natural mixing of food habits, and foods traditionally eaten in one climate and cultural setting are now often eaten in entirely different settings. Some, such as those advocating the Slow Food Movement, consider this a disadvantage, but the reality of the present situation among the Jewish people is different.

Maimonides, or Rambam, born in Cordova, Spain, discusses the ramifications of eating according to one's climate, "The warmer the temperature, the less should be the quantity, because in summertime the digestive processes are too weak to benefit from natural heat."

Though Jewish eating is often mixed today, not totally reflecting the original dietary practices of each population, a set of general guidelines for natural Jewish nutrition can be postulated based on our Jewish roots for natural nutrition in general, as discussed in Chapter 2. These guidelines, accepted by modern nutrition professionals, can be the basis for healthy eating with some adjustment for climatic or cultural preferences, if desired.

Since kashrut, the kosher system of eating, is such an intrinsic part of Jewish life, it makes us conscious of the special importance of the spiritual aspects of eating. Jewish tradition teaches us that our system of eating is Divinely inspired, and the foods affect us in spiritual ways. The Sabbath, holiday, and kabbalistic aspects of Jewish nutrition together with the various food blessings which should be recited with proper intention, again emphasize this spirituality.

The Guidelines for Natural Jewish Nutrition, then, are based on our Jewish roots and ancient food habits, as well as on the kosher system of eating and other spiritual aspects.

**Natural Jewish Nutrition – Guide to Good Eating**

This "Guide to Good Eating" includes fresh, wholesome, and colorful foods, rich in antioxidants, mostly plant-based, and minimally processed. It is naturally lower in animal fat and higher in plant fiber and nutrients. Eating these foods in modest portions naturally limits your calorie intake. Getting plenty of fresh water and daily physical exercise helps the body use nutrients, remove waste products, and maintain muscle tone and strength.

| Guide To Good Eating | |
|---|---|
| Whole Grains | Breads and cereals, especially wheat, barley, oats, rye, and spelt |
| Legumes | Lentils, chickpeas, peas, and beans |
| All Vegetables | Including colorful vegetables, dark green, white or red and sweet potatoes, and other root vegetables |
| All Fruits | Especially rich, colorful fruits and vitamin C-containing citrus and summer fruits emphasizing fruits of the Seven Species of the Land of Israel, including grapes, figs, pomegranates, olives and dates |
| Animal Products | Lower fat, limited amounts; milk, yogurt, cheeses, eggs, fish, chicken, turkey, lean meat (no skin) |
| Oils | Cold-pressed recommended: olive (or canola); alternatives: sesame, safflower, corn, soy, sunflower, nuts, and seeds |
| Beverages | Water, fresh fruit juices or fruit juice concentrates without sugar added, herbal teas, grain coffees, mineral waters, and vegetable juices |

It is recommended to avoid elements that harm the body like tobacco and excessive alcohol use. On the other hand, dry red wine, used by Jews from ancient times, is rich in antioxidants and is now thought to prevent disease.

Avoid excessive sugar intake in place of nutrient-containing foods, also fried foods, excessive caffeine-containing beverages (such as coffee and cola), and salt.

To bring out the natural taste in foods, use herbs and spices, garlic, lemon, vinegars, fruit concentrates, and honeys. Choose apples, celery, carrot sticks, raisins, vegetable soup, and oranges as healthy snacks.

Eat in a quiet, comfortable setting, whenever possible. Enjoy eating good, natural, unprocessed food, in moderation in a relaxed atmosphere.

Judaism emphasizes good health practices. The importance of adequate exercise, sleep, and relaxation in regards to health have traditionally been encouraged and have great importance.

The Rambam, the great Jewish medial authority of the past and one of the greatest Torah scholars of all times, discussed in detail the mind-body relationship in health, the use of food as medicine, the importance of regular exercise, and the negative effects of stress. He writes in "*The Preservation of Youth, Essays on Health*," as translated from Arabic by Hirsh L. Gordon, page 25, as follows:

> "One does not consider exercise, though it is the main
> principle in keeping one's health and in the repulsion of
> most illnesses." He continues that "Exercise removes the
> harm caused by most bad habits which most people have."

The Rambam discusses the importance of emotional stability and optimism on health, and the use of music and cheerful stories and laughter as beneficial to good health.

Exercise is now known to improve mood, combat chronic illness such as heart disease and osteoporosis; it helps manage weight, boosts one's energy level and promotes better sleep. A half hour to an hour a day of moderate pace walking can have tremendous health benefits. Moving your muscles can help preserve your muscle mass and will increase your muscle strength. Regular exercise helps manage stress, which in itself can be damaging to health.

Stress is a component in many illnesses, ranging from backaches to heart disease. Faith in G-d is the ultimate stress reducer, but it often requires great spiritual investment to achieve results. In the meantime, stress management techniques may help to reduce some of the negative effects of stress over time.

Fresh air, sunlight, water, progressive muscle relaxation, breathing exercises, stretching, visualization, music, meditation, and prayer are all effective relaxation techniques that can affect our physical and spiritual health.

Mind control can be achieved by constantly keeping in mind the famous, important saying, as expressed by the late Lubavitcher Rebbe (his memory should be a blessing for us all), Rabbi Menachem Mendel Schneersohn, who agreed and blessed me personally to enter the field of nutrition:

"Think good, and it will be good."

And with this, I wish to conclude my book, *Jewish Natural Nutrition... with Kabbalistic Insights*, may G-d bless you all.

*Writing this book has been an incredible experience!*
*To write creatively one must be a proper vessel.*
*The writing comes through you, inspired from Above.*
*It is an exhilarating and exhausting experience.*

# Section IV

# Recipes

*The recipes on the following pages
are from friends and family and have
been handed down for generations
as part of Jewish tradition.*

# Traditional Sabbath Foods

## Apple Compote

PREP TIME: 10 MINUTES     COOK TIME: 30 MINUTES

1 pound (½ kg.) apples
2 cups water
2 tablespoons honey

Juice of 1 lemon
Cinnamon or cloves (optional)

Peel, core and cut the apples as desired, in bite-sized pieces or sliced. Put the apples and water in a pot, and bring to a boil. Simmer covered for ½ hour. Add the honey, lemon juice, and spices. Chill and serve. Yield: 4 servings

## CHALLAH BREAD

"Challah" means dough and refers to bread made from dough that has undergone separation. There is a special "mitzvah" (religious precept) for Jewish women with its source in the Torah, requiring the head of the dough of breads to be separated and given to the priests as tithe. Since the destruction of the Temple, this "mitzvah" has been satisfied by separating a portion of the dough (a piece about the size of an olive, a "kezayit," ½ ounce or 15 grams). The separated piece is burned in the oven, and it is then wrapped and disposed of, not eaten. The separation which is symbolic sacrifice applies only when one is using a recipe whose quantities are approximately 9 to 10 cups of flour. When quantities of more than 3 pounds are used, about 12½ cups of flour, challah is separated by taking the olive-sized portion of the dough and reciting a special blessing:

> "Blessed are You, L-rd our G-d, King of the Universe, who sanctified us with His commandments, and commanded us to separate challah."

Only breads made from wheat, barley, rye, spelt and oats require separation. If you forgot to separate challah, and the bread is already baked, you can place all the loaves together, say the blessing (if an adequate amount of flour was used), and cut off a piece of one.

Challahs are normally eaten on the Sabbath and holidays, where they are served in pairs. This is symbolic of the double portions of manna received in the desert on Friday, in advance of the Sabbath, when none was received.

## Challah Bread

BAKE TEMP: 350° F (175° C)    BAKE TIME: 30 MINUTES

1 package active dry yeast          ⅛ cup oil
1 cup warm water                    1 teaspoon salt
4 cups flour                        1 egg
¼ cup sugar or 3 tablespoon honey   Sesame or poppy seeds (optional)

Mix the yeast and water in a large bowl. Add the sugar or honey, oil, and salt. Blend in the egg and then the flour, adding a small amount of flour at a time to make a soft dough. Knead the dough on a lightly floured surface until soft and elastic, about 10 minutes. Separate challah, if necessary (see explanation). Place the dough in an oiled bowl, turning it to oil all surfaces. Cover with a towel and allow to rise in a warm place until it doubles in size (about 2 hours). Punch down the dough and place it on a lightly floured surface.

Divide the dough into two equal parts and then divide each of these into three equal parts. Shape each part into a long strip. Braid the three even strips together into a loaf (as you would braid hair), and place them on a lightly oiled baking sheet. Repeat with the other three strips. Cover the loaves and allow to rise in a warm place until they are doubled in size, about 1½ hours. Brush the loaves with oil and sprinkle on sesame or poppy seeds (optional).

Bake Temp: 350° F (175° C) for about 30 minutes, or until done, browned, but not over baked. Remove from oven and allow to cool. Yield: 2 small loaves or 1 large loaf.

# Chamin – "Machshi"

PREP TIME: 30 MINUTES     COOK TIME: 2 HOURS

This is a tasty Sephardic cooked dish for the Sabbath morning meal.

10 small, finger-size squash
1 onion
2 cups uncooked rice
2 tomatoes, chopped
2 beets, sliced
1 kosher chicken, cut into eighths
1 apple, peeled and sliced

2 quinces (if available), sliced
  (optional)
3-4 dates, pitted
Juice of 1 lemon
2 tablespoons tomato paste
Seasonings (paprika, salt, black
  pepper) (optional)

Cut off the stems of the squash; carve out the inside seeds and pulp, and reserve. Brown the onion in a frying pan with little or no oil.

Prepare a mixture of the raw rice, chopped tomatoes, browned onions, and seasonings (to taste). Fill each hollowed squash with this mixture.

Put the seeds and pulp of the squash in a large pot, covering the bottom. Over this, spread a layer of beet slices; then place the cut and cleaned chicken (after removing the skin and fat). Arrange the stuffed squash on top of the chicken; and over the squash, spread the apple slices, quinces, dates, lemon juice, and tomato paste. Add enough water to cover the entire mixture.

Cover the pot, bring it to a boil, and cook 2 hours over a low fire. Transfer it to an electric Sabbath hotplate to keep it warm until the Sabbath morning meal. Yield: 6 servings.

# Gefilte Fish

PREP TIME: 30 MINUTES          COOK TIME: 1 HOUR

1 onion
1 garlic clove
1 carrot
1 lb. ground carp, whitefish,
     or other substitute
1 egg
½ teaspoon salt (optional)

½ teaspoon pepper (optional)
Sugar to taste (optional)
2 tablespoon matzah meal
Broth:
1 onion
1 carrot
Salt, pepper, sugar to taste (optional)

Grate onion, garlic, and carrot. Mix ground fish, grated onion, carrot, egg, salt, pepper, sugar, and matzah meal. With wet hands, shape the fish mixture into balls.

For the broth, fill a deep pot with water and add onion, carrot, salt, pepper, and sugar (optional). Bring to a boil and lower the heat. Gently drop the balls into the simmering broth mixture. Cover and simmer for about 1 hour. Remove and allow to cool.

Slice the cooked carrot from the broth and serve together with the fish. It is often customary to serve together with a mixture of horseradish and beets, as a traditional Sabbath dish. Yield: 12 balls

# Light Cholent

PREP TIME: 20 MINUTES          COOK TIME: 2 HOURS

8 potatoes
1 onion, sliced
2 garlic cloves, sliced
1 small kosher chicken,
     cut into portions

Mushrooms (optional)
1 cup white beans, soaked over-night,
     or 1 cup barley (optional)
2 tablespoons tomato paste (optional)
Seasonings (salt, pepper, etc.)

Peel the potatoes, onions, and garlic. Put them in a large pot with the cleaned and skinned chicken (remove all visible fat), the optional ingredients, and seasonings, and cover with water. Cover the pot, bring to a boil, and simmer over a low flame for 2 hours. Use an electric Sabbath hotplate to keep it warm until the Sabbath morning meal. Yield: 6 servings.

# Low-Fat Chicken Soup

PREP TIME: 30 MINUTES    COOK TIME: 1 HOUR

1 kosher chicken
2 onions
3 quarts water
2 carrots

2 zucchini
2 celery stalks
2 cloves garlic
2 tablespoons oil

Wash chicken and remove skin and fat. Sautée the onions for 5 minutes. Add the chicken, water, and sliced vegetables to a large pot. Bring water to a boil. Then reduce the heat and simmer for at least an hour.

This broth can be enjoyed with noodles on the Sabbath and matzah balls at Passover. Yield: 8 servings.

# Potato Knishes

BAKE TEMP: 350° F (175° C)    BAKE TIME: 20 MINUTES

For the dough:
1 cup mashed potatoes
1 tablespoon oil
1 teaspoon salt
3 cups unbleached white flour
1 teaspoon baking powder
1 teaspoon turmeric
½ cup cold water

For the filling:
1 cup chopped onions
2 tablespoon oil
3 cups mashed potatoes
1 teaspoon salt
½ teaspoon garlic powder
¼ teaspoon black pepper

For the dough, mix 1 cup mashed potatoes, 1 tablespoon oil, and 1 teaspoon salt. Add the flour, baking powder, and turmeric and mix well. Add ½ cup water and knead to a smooth dough. Cover with a cloth.

For the filling, roll out dough on a floured surface until about ¼ inch thick. Cut into 5 x 6-inch rectangles. Combine filling ingredients and place 2-3 tablespoons in each rectangle. Fold corners of dough in and pinch tight in center. Bake for about 20 minutes or until browned. Yield: 15-18 knishes.

# Potato Kugel

BAKE TEMP: 350° F (175° C)    BAKE TIME: 1 HOUR

This recipe is a staple of Eastern European Jewish cooking.

3 eggs
2 tablespoons flour
1 teaspoon salt
½ teaspoon pepper

4 medium potatoes
1 onion
¼ cup oil

In a large bowl, mix eggs, oil, flour, salt and pepper. Grate the potatoes and onion. Let stand a few minutes, and then remove any excess liquid. Add the grated potatoes to the egg-flour mixture, and mix well. Pour into an oiled baking dish and bake for about 1 hour until brown and crispy on top. Yield: 6 servings.

# Sabbath Salmon Fish

BAKE TEMP: 350° F (175° C)    BAKE TIME: 1½ HOURS

15 oz. salmon filet (baby salmon
    preferred)
1 red pepper, sliced
5 cloves garlic, sliced

½ cup ketchup or tomato sauce
½ cup mayonnaise
½ cup water
Salt and pepper to taste

Wash and place fish filet slices in a small pan. Place red pepper and garlic slices over the fish. Mix ketchup, mayonnaise, and water. Add a dash of salt and a dash of pepper. Pour the mixture over the fish. Add water to cover the fish completely. Cover with aluminum foil and bake for 1½ hours at 350° F (175° F). Uncover for ten minutes to brown. Serve hot or cold. Can place on a hotplate to keep warm for the Friday night meal, if desired. Yield: 4 servings.

# Holiday Foods

## *Applesauce*

### (No Sugar Added)

PREP TIME: 10 MINUTES    COOK TIME: 10 MINUTES

2 pounds (1 kg.) apples, unpeeled
½ cup apple or pineapple juice
½ teaspoon cinnamon, optional

Wash the apples well, cut into small pieces, and place in a large pot. Add the juice and, if desired, cinnamon, and bring to a boil. Cover pot and cook 10 minutes over a medium fire, then cool. Mash to desired consistency or process in a blender or food mill. Serve chilled. Yield: 3 cups.

## *Carrot Tzimmes*

PREP TIME: 15 MINUTES    COOK TIME: 1 HOUR

Tzimmes is traditionally eaten on Rosh Ha-Shana, The Jewish New Year, together with other sweet foods, as a sign for a sweet year.

5 large carrots, peeled          1 tablespoon oil
Orange juice to cover            10 small prunes
2 tablespoons honey              Dash of ginger (optional)

Slice the carrots, cover with orange juice in a small pot, and boil for about 10 minutes. Add the honey, oil, and whole prunes. Simmer over a low fire for about 1 hour, or until most of the liquid is absorbed. Add ginger if desired, and simmer a few minutes more. Yield: 5 servings.

# Charoset

### PREP TIME: 20 MINUTES

Charoset is traditionally eaten during the Passover seder meal.

2 cups pecans or walnuts
15 dates
6 apples, peeled and cored

½ cup kosher grape juice
or kosher wine
Cinnamon, to taste

Chop nuts, dates, and apples. Put in a bowl and mix together with the grape juice or wine and cinnamon. Yield: 12 servings.

# Chrein (Maror)

### PREP TIME: 5 MINUTES

Served at the Passover seder, Chrein is also commonly eaten with gefilte fish at the Ashkenazic Sabbath and holiday meals.

1 cup fresh horseradish root
½ cup vinegar

Blend all the ingredients in a blender. Refrigerate. Yield 2½ cups.

## Latkes (Potato Pancakes)

PREP TIME: 20 MINUTES     COOK TIME: VARIES

Jewish latkes is a favorite food of Ashkenazic Jews the entire year, but they are especially popular during Hanukah, when foods fried in oil are traditional.

| | |
|---|---|
| 6 large potatoes | 1 tablespoon salt |
| 2 onions | 3 eggs |
| ¼ cup flour | Vegetable oil (for frying) |

Grate the potatoes and onions, and press out as much liquid as possible. In a large bowl, mix with the rest of the ingredients. Heat oil in a large skillet over a medium flame. Drop 2 tablespoons of the potato mixture into the skillet for each pancake. Flatten each pancake with the back of a spoon. Fry until golden on one side, then turn over and brown on the second side. Serve with applesauce. Yield: 16-18 latkes

# Stuffed Cabbage

BAKE TEMP: 350° F (175° C)     BAKE TIME: 2 HOURS

Traditionally served during Simchat Torah, the last day of the Sukkot holiday, and on Purim.

| | |
|---|---|
| 1 pound chopped meat | ½ cup sugar |
| 2 cups cooked rice | Salt and pepper, to taste |
| 1 large head of cabbage | Raisins |
| 2 cups tomato sauce | Honey |

Cook the tomato sauce and add ½ cup sugar. Mix the rice with chopped meat. Add salt and pepper to taste. Boil the cabbage and separate the leaves. Put a little of the tomato sauce on the bottom of a large baking pan. Take a leaf of cabbage and place 2 tablespoons of the rice and meat mixture in the middle. Roll the leaf length wise and fold in the ends. Place in the sauce on the bottom of the pan. Continue in this manner until all the leaves and the mixture is used up. Pour remaining sauce over the cabbage leaves, sprinkle with raisins and drizzle a small amount of honey on top. Bake for 2 hours. Yield: 6-8 servings.

# Traditional Jewish Foods

## Bean Salad

PREP TIME: 5 MINUTES

2 cups cooked green beans
2 cups cooked yellow beans
1 pound (½ kg.) cooked red kidney
    beans (optional)
2 cups cooked chickpeas

1 onion, sliced thin
¼ cup oil
½ cup vinegar
⅓ cup honey
1 teaspoon salt

Place the beans and the chickpeas in a large bowl and add the sliced onion. Separately, combine the remaining ingredients and pour over the vegetables, mixing well. Refrigerate 3-6 hours. Yield: 10 servings.

## Beet Borscht

PREP TIME: 10 MINUTES      COOK TIME: 1 HOUR

8 large beets
2 quarts (2 liters) water
Salt to taste

2 tablespoons honey or fruit juice
    concentrate
¼ cup lemon juice

Peel the beets. Cut, dice or grate them. Combine the beets, water, salt, and honey or fruit juice concentrate, and cook for 1 hour. Add the lemon juice. Chill and serve. Yield: 8 servings

# Bubby's Granola

BAKE TEMP: 300° F (150° C)     BAKE TIME: 50 MINUTES

2½ cups regular rolled oats
½ cup slivered almonds
½ cup toasted wheat germ
½ cup sesame seeds

½ cup hulled sunflower seeds
½ cup honey
⅓ cup orange juice
½ cup raisins

In an extra-large mixing bowl combine the oats, almonds, wheat germ, sesame seeds, and sunflower seeds.

Stir together the honey and orange juice. Pour the mixture over the combined dry ingredients, stirring until evenly distributed. Spread the mixture evenly in a greased baking pan. Bake at 300° F (150° C) for 45-50 minutes or until brown, first stirring every 15 minutes, then several times during the last 15 minutes. Remove from the oven. Stir in the raisins, transfer the mixture to another pan or bowl, and cool. Store in an airtight container up to 1 month. Yield: 5 cups.

# Couscous

PREP TIME: 5 MINUTES     COOK TIME: 5 MINUTES

This is a traditional Sephardic Jewish dish, often served with chickpeas and vegetables.

1 cup couscous
3 tablespoons oil
2 cups water

Salt, pepper, paprika and garlic,
    to taste

Put couscous into a large, wide pot. Add 3 tablespoons of oil and mix. Then add 2 cups boiling water, spices, and salt, to taste. Mix well, cover, and allow to sit for 5 minutes. Fluff with a fork and allow to sit uncovered for another 5 minutes. Fluff again. Serve warm with a mixture of chickpeas and cooked vegetables. Yield: 4 servings.

# *Fruit Bars*

BAKE TEMP: 325° F (170° C)    BAKE TIME: 50 MINUTES

1 pound apples, peeled, cored
and finely chopped
2 ounces pitted dates, rinsed
and coarsely chopped
2 ounces dried apricots,
rinsed and chopped
3 ounces mixed nuts, chopped
2 ounces raisins, rinsed

1 ounce sesame seeds
2½ ounces rolled oats
1 ounce pumpkin seeds
2½ ounces whole-wheat flour
6 tablespoons unsweetened
apple juice
2 teaspoons baking powder
3 tablespoons oil

Lightly grease an 8-inch square tin.

Put the apples in a heavy-based saucepan with 1 tablespoon of water. Cover tightly and cook for about 10 minutes, until the apples are very soft. Uncover and continue to cook the apples, stirring, for an additional 2 minutes or until the excess moisture has evaporated. Add the remaining ingredients and mix together well.

Pack into the prepared tin and level the surface. Bake at 325° F (170° C) on a low shelf in the oven, for 30-40 minutes. Move the tin to the top of the oven for another 10 minutes of baking time. When completely baked, the mixture will be slightly brown around the edges and will feel firm to the touch. Mark into 8 bars while still warm. Leave to cool in the tin. When cold, turn out and cut into bars. Yield: 8 bars.

# Fruit Cake

BAKE TEMP: 350° F (175° C)    BAKE TIME: 1¼ HOURS

2 cups whole-wheat flour
1-2 cups raisins or other dried fruits
1½ teaspoons baking powder
1 teaspoon baking soda
¼ teaspoon cloves
½ teaspoon nutmeg
¼ teaspoon allspice

½ teaspoon cinnamon
1½ cups water (360 ml.)
½ cup honey or fruit juice
    concentrate (120 ml.)
¼ cup oil (60 ml.)
2 egg whites

Preheat the oven to 350° F (175° C). Oil two loaf pans. Combine the dry ingredients by hand. Combine the liquid ingredients. Mix together. Pour into loaf pans, and bake for 1 hour and 15 minutes. Yield: 2 cakes

# Fruit Salad

PREP TIME: 10 MINUTES

3 oranges
4 bananas
3 apples
Raisins or chopped dates

Juice of 1 lemon
Cloves or mint, optional
Honey or fruit juice concentrate
    (optional)

Peel and slice the oranges and bananas; cut up the apples after washing well. Add the raisins or chopped dates, and the lemon juice. If desired, add honey or fruit juice concentrate and spices, to taste. Mix well, chill, and serve. Yield: 6 servings.

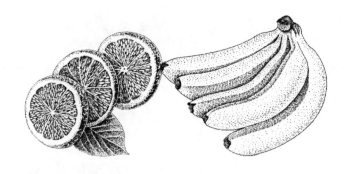

# Fruit Topping

PREP TIME: 15-25 MINUTES

2 pounds ripe fruit, pitted and sliced
¼-⅓ cup honey or fruit
    juice concentrate

1 cup water
Cloves, cinnamon, mint, etc.
    (optional)

Place the fruit and water in a saucepan, stir, and bring to a boil. Add the honey or fruit juice concentrate, spices and herbs, stir, and simmer covered for several minutes. To thicken the mixture, let it stand covered for several hours. Then cook it again over a medium fire and stir to thicken it further. One tablespoon of cornstarch dissolved in 2 tablespoons of cold water may be added, also, as a thickening agent. Yield: 4 cups.

# Gravy

PREP TIME: 20 MINUTES

2 pounds (1 kg.) vegetables
    (potato, carrots, squash, etc.)
2 cups soup stock or water
1 tablespoon whole-wheat flour,
    lightly browned, or cornstarch
1 onion, grated
3 cloves garlic, minced

Optional:
Vinegar
Tomato puree
Mushrooms
Dry wine
Lemon
Honey
Herbs or Spices

Cook the vegetables in a large pot in a small amount of water until tender. Mash the vegetables by hand or process them in a blender. Add enough liquid so as to achieve a satisfactory consistency, along with the flour or cornstarch. Add the onion and garlic. If desired, they may be first lightly sautéed in oil. Add any optional ingredients. Cook the mixture for several minutes, while stirring. Serve over grains, pastas, or vegetables. Experiment and enjoy! Yield: 6 cups.

## *High-Calcium Halvah Bar*

PREP TIME: 5 MINUTES

This recipe contains about 400 milligrams of calcium.

1 tablespoon carob powder
2 teaspoons blackstrap molasses
½ teaspoon water

2 tablespoons sesame butter
(from whole ground seeds)
Sesame seeds or wheat germ

Combine all the ingredients and stir well. Roll the mixture into a bar and coat with whole sesame seeds or wheat germ. Serve at room temperature or frozen. Yield: 1 bar (1 oz.)

## *Hummus*

PREP TIME: 5 MINUTES

Chickpea (garbanzo bean) spread, is commonly used by Jews in Israel and in the Middle East and by Sephardic Jews throughout the world.

2 cups pre-cooked chickpeas, drained
¼ cup water
2 tablespoons tahina (sesame butter )
1 tablespoon lemon juice

½ teaspoon garlic powder
½ teaspoon cumin
Salt and pepper, as desired

Blend until creamy by hand or in food processor. Serve with pita bread.

## Israeli Salad

PREP TIME: 15 MINUTES

3 cucumbers
3 tomatoes
1 green pepper
1 red pepper

2 tablespoons olive oil
1 teaspoon salt (optional)
1 teaspoon lemon juice
Chopped parsley

Finely cut all vegetables, the smaller the better, and mix in a large bowl. Add oil and lemon juice, salt and chopped parsley. Yield: 5 servings.

## Kasha Varneshkas

PREP TIME: 15 MINUTES    COOK TIME: 30 MINUTES

1 package buckwheat kasha
2 teaspoons oil
2 cups whole-wheat noodles
    (bows or other shapes)

Seasoning to taste
    (spices, sautéed onion, garlic)

Check kasha for stones, insects, and debris. Put in a large pot. Add the oil to the dry kasha, and mix well. Stir over low heat until warm and slightly browned.

Pour in boiling water (3 times the amount of dry kasha), and bring to a quick boil. Season as desired. Turn off the heat and cover. Allow kasha to soak for about 20 minutes.

Cook the noodles separately in a generous amount of boiling water until soft. Strain, rinse, and mix well with the cooked kasha. Serve warm. Yield: 8 cups.

## Lentil Soup

PREP TIME: 10 MINUTES     COOK TIME: 1¼ HOURS

1 cup lentils
1 onion, grated
4 cups water

Salt
3 cloves garlic, minced
Coriander

Combine the ingredients in a large pot and bring to a boil. Skim the foam. Simmer until lentils are soft (about 1¼ hours). Yield: 3 cups.

## Low-Fat Salad Dressing

PREP TIME: 10 MINUTES

2 tablespoons oil,
    preferably cold-pressed
Juice of 1 lemon
3 tablespoons cider vinegar
1 clove garlic, minced
½ cup water
1-2 teaspoons dried or fresh herbs,
    chopped (i.e., basil, dill,
    marjoram, parsley)

Optional:
Onion, minced
1 ripe tomato, grated
Additional garlic, minced
Additional lemon juice
Additional herbs or spices

Shake the ingredients in a tightly closed glass bottle (or blend in a food processor) before serving. The mixture may be stored several days in the refrigerator. Yield: 1 cup.

# Mejadra

PREP TIME: 5 MINUTES     COOK TIME: 1¼ HOURS

Mejadra is a traditional Middle Eastern dish.

1 cup lentils

1 cup rice (whole rice preferred)

6 cups water

½ teaspoon salt

1 onion

1 tablespoon oil

½ teaspoon cumin or turmeric

Pepper, to taste (optional)

Wash and cook the lentils in three cups water until soft. Cook the rice separately in three cups water for 30 to 40 minutes over a low flame, adding the salt. Drain. Lightly sautee an onion until browned. Then, mix the rice, lentils, and sauteed onion. Add cumin or turmeric and mix. Yield: 4 servings.

# Tahina and Oatmeal Cookies

BAKE TEMP: 375° F (190° C)     BAKE TIME: 15-30 MINUTES

½ cup honey

1 teaspoon cinnamon

½ cup chopped nuts

1½ cups rolled oats

6 tablespoons tahina (sesame butter)

Raisins (optional)

Combine all the ingredients by hand. Form little balls, and flatten with a fork dipped in water.

Bake on a greased cookie sheet in a 375° F (190° C) oven for 15-30 minutes until light brown. Do not over-bake! Yield: 30 cookies.

## Tomato Sauce

(for grain, pasta, and vegetable dishes)

PREP TIME: 20 MINUTES

1 onion, finely grated
2 cloves garlic, finely minced
1 pound (½ kg.) pureed ripe
   tomatoes, fresh or canned

1 cup water
2 teaspoons oil, preferably cold-pressed
4 teaspoons fresh or 2 teaspoons dried
   herbs (i.e., oregano, basil, thyme)

Lightly sauté the onion and garlic in oil. Add the tomatoes and water, stir well, and simmer for several minutes. Add the herbs and simmer for a few more minutes. Yield: 3 cups.

## Vegetable Soup

PREP TIME: 10 MINUTES     COOK TIME: 30 MINUTES

4 potatoes, peeled
1 onion
3 carrots, peeled
1 bunch parsley or dill

2 squash
2 cloves garlic
2 stalks celery
Salt, to taste

Blend all the ingredients in a blender. Put in a large pot, add enough water to cover vegetables, cover and cook ½ hour. Yield: 5 servings.

# Whole-Wheat Bread

PREP TIME: 40 MINUTES      RISING TIME: 90 MINUTES
BAKE TEMP: 425° F (220° C)      BAKE TIME: 50 MINUTES

3 pounds (1.4 kg.) plain
  whole-wheat flour
1 ounce (40 g.) fresh yeast or
  4½ teaspoons dry yeast

2 teaspoons salt
2 teaspoons honey

Lightly oil and flour two 2-pound (900 g.) loaf tins and set aside. Put the flour and salt in a warmed bowl, mix well and set aside.

Blend the fresh yeast and the honey with 10 fluid ounces (300 ml.) of tepid water.

If dry yeast is used, sprinkle it into 10 fluid ounces (300 ml.) of tepid water in which the honey has been blended, and leave this in a warm place for 15 minutes, until frothy.

Make a well in the center of the flour and pour in the yeast liquid. Mix well to form a firm dough, adding more tepid water as needed.

Cover the bowl containing the dough with a clean cloth. Leave it in a warm place for about 1 hour or until the dough has doubled in size.

To punch down the dough, turn it out onto a lightly floured surface and knead well for 10 minutes to remove any air bubbles. To knead, fold the dough in half. Lean into the dough using the palms of your hands. The pressure will flatten out the dough.

Turn the dough a quarter turn, fold it in half, and continue kneading. Add small amounts of flour to your hands and to the board to prevent the dough from sticking. Divide into 2 equal pieces, then shape each into a loaf. Place in the loaf tins. Cover with a towel and leave in a warm place to rise for about 30 minutes, until the loaves have almost doubled in size.

Bake at 425° F (220° C) for 40-50 minutes, until baked through. The top of each loaf should sound hallow when gently tapped. Remove from the tins and cool on a rack. Yield: two 2-pound (900 gram) loaves, 20 slices per loaf.

# Whole Wheat Pita Bread

PREP TIME: 15 MINUTES     RISING TIME 45 MINUTES
BAKE TEMP: 450° F (230° C)     BAKE TIME: 10 MINUTES

1 pound (450 g.) plain whole wheat flour
¼ teaspoon sea salt, optional
2 tablespoons olive oil

1 teaspoon dry yeast
10 fluid ounces (300 ml.)
Tepid water

Lightly oil 1 or 2 baking sheets and set aside. Mix the whole wheat flour, yeast, sea salt, and olive oil together, then add the water to make a soft but kneadable dough. Turn onto a well-floured work surface and knead for 8 minutes. Divide the dough into 8 pieces.

Using your palm, roll each piece of dough into a ball, and then, with a rolling pin, into an oval about ⅕ inch (½ cm.) thick.

Place on the baking sheet(s). Cover with a clean cloth and leave to rise in a warm place for about 45 minutes, until roughly doubled in size.

Bake at 450° F (230° C) for 10 minutes. Remove from the oven. To keep in the steam and create a soft bread, wrap well in a clean cloth or foil and set aside for at least 10 minutes. Before serving, place under a moderate grill to puff up. Yield: 8 pitas.

# Hebrew Sources

*Arvei Nachal.* Hassidic discourses on the weekly Torah portion written by Rabbi Dovid Shlomo of Zefat, Israel. He is known as the "Arvei Nachal."

*Bible.* See also *Chumash.* Known as the Written Law, it consists of the Five Books of Moses (the Pentateuch), the Prophets, and the Writings.

*Beer Mayim Chaim.* A Hassidic work written by Rabbi Chaim Tirar of Tchernovitz (1760-1817), arranged as a commentary on the weekly Torah portion.

*B'nei Yissachar.* A Hassidic text written by Rabbi Zvi Elimelech Shapiro of Dynov (1783-1841).

*Chaim Vital.* Rabbi Hayyim ben Joseph Vital (Calabria, Italy 1543-Damascus 1620) was best known as the author of the teachings of his master, the great kabbalist, Rabbi Yitzchak Luria (the Arizal) of Zefat, Israel. His "Likutei Torah" is a kabbalistic analysis of the commandments.

*Chesed l'Avraham.* A kabbalistic work by Rabbi Avraham Azulai, one of the great Torah Sages of Spain who later resided in Chevron.

*Chumash* (Genesis, Exodus, Leviticus, Numbers, Deuteronomy). The five books of the Torah given by G-d to the Jewish people on Mount Sinai.

*Commentary on the Torah* by Rabbi Moshe ben Nachman (the Ramban, 1135-1204). One of the leading spiritual leaders of his time, the Ramban headed a yeshiva in Gerona, Spain, and wrote over fifty works on the Torah, the Talmud, Jewish law, philosophy, Kabbalah, and medicine.

*Da'as Tevunos.* A kabbalistic work by Rabbi Moshe Chayim Luzzatto (the Ramchal, 1701-1745), who, following the controversy caused in his native Italy by his kabbalistic writings, moved to Amsterdam, where he wrote his highly acclaimed *Mesillas Yesharim* (*The Path of the Righteous*), a step-by-step program for any Jew to attain moral perfection.

*Ein Yaakov.* A collection of all the inspirational and ethical, non-legal, teachings in the Talmud together with commentaries. It was compiled by Rabbi Jacob ibn Habib and his son Rabbi Levi ibn Habib.

Eisen, Yosef. *Miraculous Journey: A Complete History of the Jewish people from Creation to the Present.* Southfield, MI: Targum/Feldheim; 2004.

*Five Books of Moses.* Known as the Pentateuch, it consists of five parts: Genesis, Exodus, Leviticus, Numbers, and Deuteronomy. Each part is further divided for weekly readings.

*Gemara.* Part of the Talmud, it includes commentaries on the Mishna.

*Halachos.* A halachic, kabbalistic work by Rabbi Yosef Chaim, the "Ben Ish Chai" of Bagdad.

*Hilchos De'os.* A chapter of the Rambam's *Mishneh Torah* (see below) which presents the laws and views of the Torah on human behavior.

*Kaf ha-Chaim.* A Code of Jewish Law consisting of ten volumes including views of many kabbalistic sages. The author was Rabbi Yaakov Chaim Sofer (1870-1930) a great Talmudist and Kabbalist. Born in Bagdad, he later settled in Jerusalem where he composed his works.

Kaplan, Aryeh. *Meditation and Kabbalah.* York Beach, ME: Samuel Weiser; 1982.

*Kedushat Levi.* A popular Hassidic text arranged according to the weekly Torah portions, written by Rabbi Levi Yitzchak of Berdichev (1740-1810).

*Kitzur Shulchan Aruch.* A widely used, lucid abridgment of the *Shulchan Aruch* (see below), written in Hungary by Rabbi Shelomo Ganzfried (1804-1886).

*Kol Menachem.* A hassidic work by the present Kaliver Rebbe of Jerusalem.

*Likutei Torah.* Hassidic discourses on the Hebrew Bible written by Rabbi Shneur Zalman of Liadi, Russia, the first Lubavitcher Rebbe, known as the "Baal Ha-Tanya."

*Magen Avraham.* A commentary on the *Orach Chayim* of the *Shulchan Aruch* (see below), written by Rabbi Avraham Abeli ben Chayim Halevi Gombiner of Kalish (d. 1683), one of the great sages of Poland.

*Maharsha.* (Chiddushei Halachot) A commentary on the Talmud written by Rabbi Samuel Eidels from Poland (1555-1631).

*Mechiltah.* Midrash of legal aspects of the Bible's Book of Exodus.

*Menachem Tzion.* Written by Rabbi Menachem Mendel of Rimanov (1745-1815) was an important Hassidic leader in Poland.

*The Midrash.* A generic term that usually refers to the non-legalistic teachings of the Rabbis of the Talmudic era. In the centuries following the final draft of the Talmud (550 C.E.), much of this material was gathered into collections known as midrashim.

*Midrash Rabbah (Bereshis Rabbah, Shemos Rabbah, Devarim Rabbah,* cited). A midrashic work (see *The Midrash,* above) arranged by the amora, Rabbi Oshia Rabbah.

*Midrash Tanchuma.* A midrashic work written by the Rabbi Tanchuma.

*Midrash Tehillim.* A midrashic commentary on the Book of Psalms, also known as "Shocher Tov Midrash Tehillim," of unknown origin.

*The Mishna.* As part of the Oral Law (The Talmud), it consists of six sections: Seeds, Festivals, Women, Damages, Holy Things, and Purities. The Mishna was compiled and written down in the 2nd century C.E.

*Mishna Brurah.* A monumental Code of Jewish Law, printed in six volumes. The author was Rabbi Yisroel Meir Kagan, known as the "Chofetz Chaim" (Poland, 1838-1933); authoritative reference on Jewish daily living.

*Mishna Torah.* The most comprehensive and succinct guide to all the laws of the Torah and the greatest work of Rabbi Moshe ben Maimon (the Rambam, 1135-1204), also known as the *Yad ha-Chazakah.* Born in Cordova, Spain, to a distinguished Rabbinical family, the Rambam was the greatest codifier in Jewish history, as well as being a Rabbinic adjudicator, a torah commentator, a philosopher, and a physician. The Rambam also wrote a commentary to the Mishneh, *Sefer ha-Mitzvos* (a classification of the 613 commandments), and *Moreh Nevuchim* (*Guide to the Perplexed,* intended to help the student who was struggling with the seeming contradictions between science and philosophy and the Torah).

*Mor v'Shemesh.* A hassidic classic by Rabbi Aharon ben Kalonimus of Krakow (d. 1882).

*Or Ha-Chaim.* A popular commentary on the Bible (Five Books of Moses). The author was Rabbi Chaim ibn Attar, a great Talmudist and Kabbalist (1696-1743). Born at Mequenez, Morocco, he later settled in Jerusalem.

*Perek Shirah.* An early baraisa that shows how the entire creation sings praise to G-d, included in the midrashic work *Yalkut Shemoni* (see *The Midrash*).

*Peri Tzaddik.* A major hassidic work by Rabbi Tzaddok Hakohen of Lublin (d. 1905), who, while closely following the thinking of the Talmudic Sages and referring to history, created a unique form of hassidism in his five volumes of sermons on the Sabbath and holiday portions.

*Pesikta Zutra.* A midrashic commentary on the Pentateuch (Five Books of Moses), also known as "Midrash Lekah Tov." It was written by Rabbi Tobia ben Eliezer, who lived in the 11th century in Castoria, Greece.

*Pirkei Avos* (*Ethics of the Fathers*). A Mishna tractate in the order of *Nezikin.* The Fathers are the early Talmudic Sages (c. 300 B.C.E.- 200 C.E.) who composed the wise, moral sayings.

*Pirkei d'Rabbi Eliezer.* An important midrashic work (see *The Midrash*, above) by the school of Rabbi Eliezer ben Hyrcanus (c. 100 C.E.), first published in Constantinople in 1514.

*Psalms.* 150 sacred poems by King David; a book of the Hebrew Bible.

*Rabbenu Bachaya.* Also known as Bahye ben Asher, he lived from the mid-thirteenth century until 1340 in Saragossa, Spain. His principle work was his commentary on the Torah (The Five Books of Moses), where he is noted for introducing kabbalah (Jewish mysticism) into this study.

*Rabbenu Chananel.* Rabbi Hananel ben Hushiel (Kirouan, North Africa, 11th century) is the author of a summarizing commentary on many tractates of the Talmud, located on the outside margin in the published text.

*Rashi.* (Rabbi Shelomo ben Yitzchak Yarchi, 1040-1105). Author of the foremost commentaries on the *Chumash* and *Gemara* (Talmud). His commentary on the *Chumash* is the first known Hebrew book published (in Rome, 1470). Rashi headed famous yeshiva academies in Troyes and Worms in France.

*Reshis Chachmah.* An ethics book written by Rabbi Eliyahu ben Moshe Vidash, a student of Rabbi Moshe Cordovero (see below, *Siddur Tefillah l'Moshe*).

*Ruach Chayim.* A commentary on *Pirkei Avos* (see above) by Rabbi Chayim of Volozhin (1749-1827), the leading student of the Vilna Gaon, and the founder of the first great Lithuanian yeshiva in Volozhin.

Scheindlin, Raymond P. *A Short History of the Jewish people: From Legendary Times to Modern Statehood.* Oxford, England: Oxford University Press; 2000.

*Seder Tu b'Shevat* (*Peri Etz Hadar*). A course of study traditionally recited by Sephardic Jews during the eating of the Tu b'Shevat fruits.

*Sefer Recanti.* A commentary on the Hebrew Bible, written by Rabbi Menachem Recanti, an Italian legalist and mystic of the late 13th and early 14th century.

*Sefer Tzioni.* A commentary on the Hebrew Bible, written by Rabbi Menachem Tzioni, published in Lemberg in 1882 with many kabbalistic insights.

*Sekhel Tov.* A midrashic work written by Rabbi Menachem ben Solomon ben Isaac (12th century).

*Sha'ar ha-Kavanos.* A kabbalistic work by Rabbi Chayim Vital (1547-1629).

*Shir ha-Shirim. The Song of Songs.* A love song to G-d by King Solomon.

*Shulchan Aruch.* The *Code of Jewish Law,* compiled by Rabbi Yosef Karo (1488-1575), a concentration of halachic conclusions of the author's *Beis Yosef,* which is based on the *Tur* or *Arba'ah Turim* of Rabbi Ya'akov ben Asher. Rabbi Karo, born in Spain, became chief Rabbi of Tzefas, Israel. He based his decisions on the Rambam, the Rosh, and the Rif; composed in four parts:

1. *Orach Chayim* contains all the laws that a Jew must perform daily (including on Sabbath and holidays), from the moment he opens his eyes in the morning until he closes them at night.

2. *Yoreh De'ah* contains all the laws regulating daily life that are not necessarily performed every day, such as kosher slaughter and the intricacies of kosher eating and drinking.

3. *Even Ha-Ezer* contains laws regulating relations between men and women.

4. *Choshen Mishpat* contains all the laws governing conduct between man and his fellow man. With the addition of the *Haga'ah,* legal decisions written by Rabbi Moshe Issserlis, who presents the Ashkenazic interpretation and tradition, the *Shulchan Aruch* became the standard halachic guide for all Jews today.

*Shulchan ha-Tahor.* A large hassidic treatise on the moral correction made by eating with proper intention and blessings, written by Rabbi Aharon Roth, the founder of the Toldos Aharon dynasty.

*Shulchan shel Arba'ah.* A concise guide to the laws of eating and drinking at the weekday and Sabbath table, written by Rabbenu Bachya ben Asher (1263-1340), Rabbinical judge and preacher in Spain who wrote commentaries on the Torah and a kabbalistic work called *Kad ha-Kemach.*

*Siddur Tefillah l'Moshe.* The edition of the prayer book prepared by Rabbi Moshe Cordovero, the leading sixteenth-century kabbalist in Tzefas.

*Siduro shel Shabbos.* A hassidic text providing much inspiration and understanding of the holiness of the Sabbath. It was written by Rabbi Chaim Tirar of Tchernovitz (1760-1817), who is also known as the "Be'er Mayim Chaim."

*The Talmud.* The body of teaching that comprises the commentary and discussion of the early Talmudic Sages on the Mishna of Rabbi Yehudah Hanasi. The study of the Mishna was actively pursued in two centers: the Land of Israel and Babylon. As a result, two distinct versions of the Talmud emerged: the Jerusalem Talmud (whose compilation was completed in Tiveriya (Tiberius) at the beginning of the fifth century C.E.) and the Babylonian Talmud (whose compilation was completed at the end of the fifth century C.E.). Tractates of the Talmud cited in this book include: *Beitzah* – laws of festivals; *Berachos –*

laws of blessings; *Kesubbos* – laws of marriage contracts; *Kilayim* – laws of forbidden hybridization and grafting; *Orlah* – laws on the first three years of fruit trees; *Pesachim* - laws of Pesach and the paschal sacrifice; *Rosh Hashana* – laws of the New Year; *Shabbos* – laws of the Sabbath; *Shevi'is* – agricultural laws for the sabbatical year; *Sotah* – laws of infidelity.

*Ta'anis.* Laws of fasting

*Tamei Ha-Mitzvos l'Zemach Zedek.* A Hassidic work written by the third Lubavitcher Rebbe, Rabbi Menachem Mendel Schneersohn (1789-1866)

*Tanna d'Vei Eliyahu.* An early midrash (see *The Midrash*, above) attributed to the teachings of the Prophet Eliyahu (Elijah). First printed in Venice in 1598.

*Tehillim.* A poetic work compiled by King David, including psalms of the ten elders: Adam, Malki Tzedek, Avraham (Abraham), Moshe (Moses), Haimon, Yedusun, Asaf, and the three sons of Korach.

*Tikkun Yissachar.* A halachic work written by Rabbi Yissachar Sussan, one of the great Sephardic rabbis of Tzefas.

*Yalkut Shimoni.* A compilation of midrashim arranged according to the weekly portions of the Hebrew Bible. The author is of uncertain identity.

*Yesod v'Shoresh ha-Avodah.* A kabbalistic last will and testament prepared by Rabbi Alexander Ziskind for his students and published in Warsaw in 1913. In reviewing the moral conduct of his life, Rabbi Ziskind finds himself guilty of having eaten more than was necessary to sustain his study of Torah.

*Zikkukin d'Nura u'Vi'urin d'Esha.* A kabbalistic work, both exoteric and esoteric, by Rabbi Shemuel Hida, first published in Prague in 1675 and endorsed by the leading scholars of the time.

*Ziv ha-Zohar.* A commentary on the *Zohar* by Rabbi Yehuda Rosenberg from Warsaw, Poland.

*Zohar*, Meaning "splendor," the *Zohar* is the major work of kabbalah in the form of discussions of second-century Land of Israel rabbinical scholars, led by Rabbi Shimon bar Yochai.

# Glossary

Abraham (Avraham, Hebrew): The first Jew, the founder of Judaism. The first of the three Patriarchs.

Adam: The first man

Ari: Refers to Rabbi Yitzhak Luria, the greatest kabbalist of modern times of Zefat, Israel.

Ashkenazic Jews or Ashkenazim: Jews from Germany and Eastern Europe and their descendants. Daily conversation was often in Yiddish. Most Jews in America are Ashkenazic.

B.C.E.: Before the Common (or Christian) Era.

Ba'al Shem Tov: Hebrew for "Master of the Good Name." Rabbi Yisroel ben Eliezar was the founder of Hassidic Judaism.

Basari: Hebrew for meaty foods in the kosher system.

Behemoth: Also known as "Shor ha-Bar." The primordial Wild Ox from the time of Creation, which tradition teaches will be served at the Feast of the Righteous in the World-to-Come.

Beit Hillel: Hebrew for "House of Hillel." A school of thought during the Talmudic period, generally reflecting the more lenient view in contrast with Beit Shammai.

Beit Shammai: Hebrew for "House of Shammai." A school of thought during the Talmudic period, generally reflecting the stricter view in contrast with Beit Hillel.

Bible: Also referred to as the "Tanach" or the Written Law. The Jewish Bible more or less corresponds to what non-Jews refer to as the "Old Testament."

Bikkurim: First fruits brought to the ancient Jerusalem Temple on the Feast of Weeks (Shavuot holiday).

Brit Milah: Hebrew for "Covenant of Circumcision." The ritual circumcision of a Jewish male child generally, health permitting, on the eighth day of his life, or of a male convert to Judaism. It is often referred to as a "bris" or "brit."

Borscht: A beet soup or juice containing ground or shredded beets, common in Russian or Ashkenazic cuisine.

C.E.: Common (or Christian) Era.

Chalavi: Hebrew for milky foods in the kosher system.

Chametz: Hebrew for a leavened grain product which is not eaten or owned by Jews during the Passover holiday.

Challah: A braided bread which is served on the Sabbath and holidays; refers to the commandment to set aside a portion of dough from breads.

Chamin: Tasty Sephardic dish for the Sabbath morning meal containing meat, rice, and vegetables. To keep it warm it is covered and set on an electric hot-plate before the beginning of the Sabbath, where cooking is forbidden.

Charoset: Traditional dish served at the Passover seder consisting of cubed apples, ground nuts, and wine to remind us of the building blocks and mortar which we used to build the Egyptian pyramids during our enslavement.

Chava: Hebrew for "Eve," the first woman.

Cholent: A tasty Ashkenazic dish for the Sabbath morning meal, containing meat or chicken, potatoes and often beans and barley.

Cholov Yisroel: Refers to dairy products whose total preparation from the milking through the packaging is supervised by reliable Jewish authorities.

Chrein: Yiddish for ground horseradish, commonly eaten by Ashkenazic Jews, mixed with beet juice and often served with gefilte fish (fish balls).

Chumash: The Five Books of Moses, also referred to as the Pentateuch.

613 Commandments: Judaism teaches that G-d gave the Jews 613 commandments which are binding on Jews but not on non-Jews. (Non-Jews have "The Seven Commandments of the Children of Noah.")

Dekel: Yiddish for a cloth used to cover the Challah breads on the Sabbath table. It symbolizes the layer of dew that covered the manna each morning in the Sinai desert after the Jews fled Egyptian slavery.

Divine Presence: Shechina in Hebrew; refers to G-d's presence in our world.

Dovid: Hebrew for David. Refers to King David, author of the psalms.

Elijah the Prophet: In Hebrew, "Eliyahu ha-Navi." Father of kabbalah, tradition relates that he ascended to Heaven alive on a chariot of fire and returns to teach the righteous secrets of the Torah and attends all ritual circumcisions.

Eshel Avraham: Hebrew for "Tree of Abraham." A special tree that the Patriarch Abraham used to test his many guests for idol worship, before providing them with hospitality.

Eve: Chava in Hebrew, the first woman.

Farfel: Yiddish for a dish of boiled clumps of flour. It is often served at the Friday night meal by Ashkenazic Jews to symbolize the manna.

Feast of Weeks: The holiday of Shavuot, commemorating the giving of the Torah and the harvest of the first fruits.

Five Books of Moses: Also referred to as the "Chumash" of the Pentateuch. It is the first part of the Written Law.

Fleisig: Yiddish for meaty foods in the kosher system.

Garden of Eden: The location of paradise, where Adam and Eve lived.

G-d: A way of avoiding writing the name of G-d, to avoid the sin of erasing or defacing the Name out of respect.

Gefilte fish: Yiddish for "stuffed fish." An Ashkenazic Jewish dish consisting of a ball or cake of chopped fish, often served on the Sabbath and holidays.

Gemara (Gemorrah): Commentaries on the Mishna. The Mishna and the Gemara together comprise the Talmud, and are referred to as the Oral Law.

Gematria: Systems of numerical equivalents to derive hidden meanings from Hebrew words.

Gilgul: Hebrew for reincarnation, where souls return to the world.

Halvah: A bar of crushed sesame seeds and sugar common in the Middle East.

Hamentashen: Yiddish for "Haman's pockets." Triangular, poppy seed or fruit-filled cookies traditionally eaten during the Purim holiday.

Hanukah (Chanukah): Hebrew for "dedication." An eight day holiday commemorating the rededication of the ancient Jerusalem Temple after it was captured and defiled by the Greeks.

Hasidism (Chasidism, Hassidism): From the word "Hasid" meaning "pious." A branch of Judaism founded by the Baal Shem Tov, Rabbi Yisroel ben Eliezar, emphasizing serving the Creator with joy and the great value of the common man.

Havdalah: Hebrew for "separation." A ceremony at the close of the Sabbath symbolizing the separation between the holy and the profane.

Hechsher: A symbol or insignia on foods or other products testifying that these items satisfy Jewish dietary laws and are kosher.

Heichal: Inner chamber of the ancient Temple in Jerusalem.

Horev: Mount Sinai where Moses received the Torah.

Hummus: Ground chickpea spread commonly eaten with pita bread by Sephardic Jews and by people in Israel and worldwide.

Isaac: Yitzchak in Hebrew. Son of Abraham and father of Jacob (Yaakov or Israel). The second of the three Patriarchs of Judaism.

Israel: The land that G-d promised to Abraham and his descendants. Alternate name for the Patriarch Jacob.

Jacob (Israel, Yisroel or Ya'akov in Hebrew). Son of Isaac, father of twelve sons, who represent the twelve tribes of Israel. The third Patriarch of Judaism.

Jerusalem: The holiest city in Judaism. King David's capitol and the location of King Solomon's Temple and the Second Temple. From ancient times Jews have faced Jerusalem during prayer throughout the world, and have prayed daily for a return to Israel and Jerusalem.

Jew: A person whose mother was a Jew or a convert to Judaism.

Judaism: The religion of the Jewish people.

Kabbalah: Jewish mystical tradition.

Kasha Varneshkas: Yiddish for a dish of buckwheat and noodles eaten by Ashkenazic Jews.

Kashrut (or Kashrus): Hebrew for "fit" or "proper." The Jewish system of dietary laws (kosher).

Kav: A unit of measure in the Torah.

Kavannah: Hebrew for "concentration" or "intent." Refers to the frame of mind required for prayer or performance of a mitzvah (commandment).

Kelipot (or Kelipos): Hebrew for husks, represents the opposite of holiness.

Kesuvim: The Writings, part of the Tanach or Written Law.

Kiddush: Hebrew for "sanctification." Special prayer said over wine at the beginning of the Sabbath or holiday meal.

Kneidelach: Yiddish for "dumplings" or matzah balls.

Knish: Yiddish for a potato and flour dumpling filled with potato and onion, chopped liver or cheese.

Kosher: Hebrew for "fit" or "proper." Food that is permissible to eat under Jewish dietary laws. Can also refer to other objects or acts that are fit according to Jewish law.

**Kugel:** Yiddish for "pudding." A casserole of potato, onion, egg or noodles, fruit, and nuts in an egg-based pudding. It is commonly served in Ashkenazic cuisine on the Sabbath and holidays, or on other festive occasions.

**Latkes:** Potato pancakes customarily eating during Hanukah.

**L'chaim:** Hebrew for "to life," it is a traditional toast on an alcoholic beverage.

**Livyatan:** Giant primordial fish which tradition relates will be served at the Feast of the Righteous in the World-to-Come (also known as Tannin).

**L-rd:** A name of G-d which is written to avoid erasing or defacing the Name.

**Luz:** A special bone at the base of the skull, named after the ancient city of Luz, where no man ever died within its boundaries. Tradition has it that this bone does not decay in the grave, and from this bone man will be brought back to life in the times of the revival of the dead.

**Man:** Hebrew for "manna," the bread which fell at night during the forty years Jews wandered in the Sinai desert after fleeing from Egyptian bondage.

**Mandelach:** Yiddish for soup nuts.

**Manna** (see Man)

**Masechta:** Hebrew for "tractate," a subdivision of the order or "seder" of the Mishna in the Oral Law.

**Mashiach:** Hebrew for "anointed" refers to the Messiah. Our redeemer, a man chosen by G-d, a descendant of King David, whose coming will be heralded by the Prophet Elijah. He will put an end to evil in the world, rebuild the Temple, bring the exiles to Israel, and usher in the World-to-Come.

**Matzah (or Matzoh):** Unleavened wheat cracker-like bread of non-risen dough eaten during the year and specially made kosher for the Passover holiday when no leavened products are permitted by Jewish law.

**Mayin nukvin:** Aramaic for "feminine waters," a kabbalistic concept.

**Melave Malka:** An additional meal traditionally eaten after the close of the Sabbath and the havdalah ceremony, known as "King David's meal."

**Menorah:** An olive oil lamp used in the ancient Jerusalem Temple. An eight-branched replica is now used in Jewish homes in commemoration of the Hanukah festival.

**Midrash:** From the Hebrew root meaning "to study" or "to investigate." Stories on writings in the Bible used to derive a principle of Jewish law or to teach a moral lesson.

Mikveh (or Mikvah): A ritual bath used for spiritual purification.

Milchig: Yiddish for dairy foods. Should not be eaten with meat by Jews.

Mishna: An early compilation of the Oral Law, part of the Talmud.

Mispar katan: In the gematria numerical system for interpreting the Torah, when there is a reduction of the tens or hundreds, dropping the zeros (for example, "yud" the numerical equivalent of 10, as it is the tenth letter of the Hebrew alphabet, becomes 1).

Mitzvot (singular, Mitzvah): Hebrew for "commandments." Refers to the 613 commandments of the Torah. Also used generally to refer to a good deed.

Moses (Moshe): Our teacher and receiver of the Torah on Mount Sinai.

Mussar: Ethical writings of the Torah.

Na'aseh V'nishma: Refers to the Jewish people's agreement to perform the Torah's commandments even before hearing them at Mount Sinai.

Nevi'im: Hebrew for "The Prophets," the second part of the Written Law.

Omer: A unit of measure (about three quarts), translated as a "sheaf."

Oneg Shabbos: Hebrew for "Sabbath delight." Generally refers to tasty food or sleep on the Sabbath.

Oral Law: As opposed to the Written Law, it refers to the Talmud which consists of the Mishna and the Gemara. The Oral Law was initially passed down orally from generation to generation.

Order: One of the six sections of the Mishna (see "Seder").

Orlah: Refers to forbidden fruit during the first three years of growth of a tree.

Pareve: Yiddish for neutral. Refers to non-meat, non-dairy foods, which may be eaten with either meat or dairy meals.

Passover (Pesach): Holiday commemorating the Exodus from Egypt.

Patriarchs: The forefathers of Judaism, Abraham, Isaac, and Jacob.

Pentateuch: The Five Books of Moses.

Pita: A round bread, hollow in the center, common in Middle East cuisine.

Preserved wine: See Yayin ha-Meshumar.

Prophets: Second of three parts of the Written Law or Tanach.

Purim: Holiday rejoicing the fall of Haman and the deliverance of the Jews by Mordechai and Queen Esther in Persia, during the period between the First and the Second Temples.

Rabbi: A religious teacher authorized to make decisions of Jewish law.

Ramak: Rabbi Moshe Cordevero, one of the greatest theoretical kabbalists of Zefat, Israel.

Rambam: Rabbi Moshe be Maimon, one of the greatest medieval Jewish scholars and physicians. Also known as Maimonides.

Rashi: Rabbi Shlomo Yitzchaki, one of the greatest medieval Jewish scholars and commentators.

Rebbe: Usually translated as "Grand Rabbi." Generally refers to the leader of a Hassidic community.

Rosh Hashana: Hebrew for "head of the year." Refers to the Jewish New Year.

Sabbath: The Jewish day of rest from before sundown on Friday evening until sunset on Saturday night. Consult local rabbis for the exact times.

Seder: Order or section of the Mishna in the Oral Law. Also refers to the festive ceremonial meal at the beginning of the Passover holiday.

Sefirot (or Sefiros): Hebrew for "emanations." Spiritual manifestations of the Creator through which He conducts His world.

Sephardic Jews: Jews from Spain, Portugal, North Africa and the Middle East and their descendants.

Seven Species: Seven types of grain or fruits representative of the produce of the Land of Israel.

Shabbat (or Shabbos): Hebrew for the Jewish Sabbath or Saturday, our day of rest and spiritual enrichment.

Shaul: Hebrew for King Saul.

Shavuot (or Shavuos): The Festival of Weeks, a holiday commemorating the giving of the Torah and the harvest of the first fruits.

Shechina: Refers to G-d's Divine Presence.

Shechitah: Kosher slaughter.

Shemittah: The Sabbatical year, every seventh year in the Land of Israel, when we do not work the land.

Shimon bar Yochai: Author of the Zohar, one of the main texts of Jewish mysticism.

Shlomo: King Solomon (son of King David) built the First Temple in Jerusalem.

Shmuel: Refers to the Prophet Samuel.

Shochet: Certified kosher slaughterer.

Shor ha-bar: The primordial Wild Ox, which tradition teaches whose meat will be served to the righteous at the feast in the World-to-Come.

Succot (Sukkot, Succos): The Festival of Booths.

Tahina (or Techina): Sesame paste common in Middle Eastern cuisine.

Talmud: The Oral Law, consisting of the Mishna and the Gemara.

Tanach: The Written Law, consisting of the Five Books of Moses, the Prophets, and the Writings.

Tannin: Also known as Leviathan or Livyatan in Hebrew, it refers to a giant primordial fish which tradition says will be served at the feast or the righteous in the World-to-Come.

Terumah: Separation of a small amount of produce once given to the priests in the ancient Jerusalem Temple. It is now physically separated from produce of the Land of Israel and respectfully discarded.

Tiferes (or Tiferet): One of the kabbalistic spheres which refers to the attribute of mercy and beauty. It is also associated with balance and healing and is representative of the Patriarch Yaakov (Jacob).

Tisha B'Av: The ninth day of the Hebrew month of Av, it is the day of destruction of both the First and the Second Ancient Temples of Jerusalem. It is traditional for Jews to fast on this day in mourning.

Torah: The Five Books of Moses or the Pentateuch. In a broader sense, it often refers to the entire body of Jewish teachings.

Torah scroll: A scroll of parchment upon which is hand-written the Five Books of Moses by a trained Jewish scribe. It is generally placed in a holy arch in the front of the synagogue out of respect.

Tractate: In Hebrew a "masechta," referring to a subdivision of an order or "seder" of the Mishna.

Tree of Knowledge: A tree in the Garden of Eden where Adam and Eve were commanded not to eat, but nevertheless, from which they did eat and were punished.

Tree of Life: A tree in the Garden of Eden giving eternal life, which was never eaten from. Also refers to a kabalistic symbol representing the ten mystical spheres.

Trefah: Non-kosher.

Tu B'Shevat: Festival of the Trees. Marks the yearly beginning of the re-growth of the fruit trees in the Land of Israel.

Tzimmes: Yiddish for an Ashkenazic dish containing carrots, prunes, honey, and oil.

World-to-Come: According to Jewish tradition, there is belief in a future world of perfection where there will be only good.

Written Law: Refers to the Five Books of Moses, the Prophets, and the Writings, all of which were originally written down.

Writings: Third part of the Written Law.

Yaakov: Jacob (Israel), son of Isaac. Father of twelve sons, who represent the tribes of Judaism. The third of the three Patriarchs of Judaism.

Yayin ha-meshumar: Hebrew for "preserved wine." A special wine from the first grapes of Creation which tradition says will be served to the righteous at the feast in the World-to-Come.

Yiddish: A language spoken for over a thousand years by mainly Ashkenazic Jews.

Yitzchak: Isaac in Hebrew, son of Abraham, and father of Jacob. The second of the three Patriarchs of Judaism.

Yom Kippur: The Jewish Day of Atonement, traditionally set aside for fasting and repentance.

Zohar: One of the most famous kabalistic texts, written by Rabbi Shimon bar Yochai.

CPSIA information can be obtained at www.ICGtesting.com
Printed in the USA
LVOW080306081212

310273LV00003B/22/P